THE LOST TRAIN

An FVP Books Anthology

Edited by
SHERI J. KENNEDY

FreeValley Publishing
North Bend, Washington
freevalleypublishing.com

ISBN: 9798672087481

DEDICATION

With hope that cooperative spirits and seeking common ground will bring well-being to all.

CONTENTS

GRATITUDE

What a pleasure it is to work with the Authors of FreeValley Publishing / FVP Books and the Artists of North Bend Art & Industry! During the whole of this anthology project I was surrounded by generous spirit, freely shared cooperation, and unquenchable enthusiasm – not to mention immense creativity and talent.

I'd like to thank all the authors and artists for their finely crafted contributions to the community. It's my privilege to present their works in this book. And also for their kindness to me and to each other, which was especially needed while isolated by Stay-at-Home orders during this project. What a joy to create this gift together!

I'm grateful to Beth Burrows and Debra Landers for coordinating the connection of FVP with NBA&I artists. And I'd like to give a special shout out to Ellen Rowan for enhancing the experience of the Artist/Author teams with promos of the pairings, and for collecting and coordinating photos of the final artworks. Also, special thanks to Tara Sreekumar - plentyopixels.com, for providing photography services and several photo images for the anthology.

And thanks to You, for showing your support for the Arts through your purchase of *THE LOST TRAIN* anthology. We appreciate it!

-Sheri J. Kennedy, Editor

INTRODUCTION

This project came about as the wish of FreeValley Publishing / FVP Books' authors to create an anthology of short stories that would benefit a local Arts group. FVP Books is a co-op of traditionally and self-published authors based in Snoqualmie Valley. As such, they decided the newly formed non-profit group, North Bend Art & Industry, would be a fun and worthwhile organization to support.

One of the authors recalled how enriching it had been to partner with the Mt. Si Arts Guild for a writing project inspired by artworks. So FVP asked NBA&I if their artists would be interested in a collaborative project. Delighted is an understatement!

The artists and authors were assigned partners. They interacted or not – as their pair agreed – during creation of their pieces. All the finished work was freely submitted to the anthology for FVP to publish. And all profits from the book will be donated to NBA&I to support their building projects and the furthering of their mission to support local Arts and artists.

The theme, the lost train, was interpreted widely and has brought together a multi-textured whole. The book holds an abundant diversity of visions, styles, genres and ideas for all ages.

As editor, I grappled with how to bring order to creations with such a variety of moods. I found the answer in author Jeffrey Cook's story, "Railway Tales," the first story in the book. It set the pattern for ordering the rest. A lovely ebb and flow from mysterious to frightening, whimsical to humorous, thought-provoking to mysterious and a good dose of heart-warming fun. That's the journey you'll take when you climb aboard *THE LOST TRAIN*.

-Sheri J. Kennedy, Editor

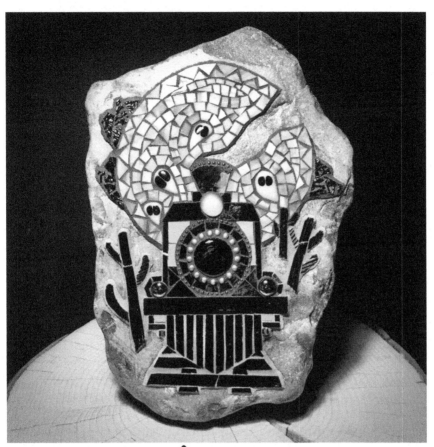

HEAD ON ⊗ Lesia Tiongson

Lesia Tiongson   Jeffrey Cook

Lesia's Inspiration: This piece is meant to evoke a sense of mystery and surprise. It is an old train in an unexpected and remote location. It reflects the glow of a full moon illuminating the lost spirits within. It feels like a mirage. Is it real? Where did it come from? It's charging your way, yet you feel immobilized, unable to react.

Lesia's Partnership: I added elements the author hoped to include in his story which were 1. A classic old west bandits on horseback train robbery 2. A mystery akin to Murder on the Orient Express and 3. evoking ghost stories.

Jeffrey's Partnership: While we didn't end up getting to collaborate a lot, the process of working with the artist was still a fun one. I tried to give her a lot of free reign, while playing with themes of ghosts, mysteries, and old West train robberies. She really delivered, I think!

Jeffrey's Inspiration: "Railway Tales" is a brief venture into childhood whimsy. Jeff spent a lot of his youth near train tracks while moving all over the country, and has memories of old, abandoned stretches of tracks leading to who-knows-where, empty cars covered in graffiti and left to sit, and train whistles in the middle of the night. All of those had influence on the story, and trying to remember those things from the perspective of an imaginative kid.

RAILWAY TALES
YOUNG ADULT FICTION
by Jeffrey Cook

"Oh wow, this is so cool. Thank you, Ms. W!" called Riley. The dark-haired girl skipped along the partially grown-over railroad tracks, heading for the thicker collections of trees.

"I'd do anything for you girls – and exploring. Just don't get too far ahead," called Angie Walker. She and her wife had been like second and third mothers to Riley Dane and Emma Arquette – and actual mothers to Cam Walker, Angie's daughter from her first marriage. A decade ago the trio had been daisies in girl scouts together. Angie had stepped in as den mother – and they'd been inseparable ever since.

"Where do you think the tracks lead?" Emma asked. The smallest of the trio, she was also the most bookish. Ever since Cam found the semi-hidden tracks during a family nature hike, Emma had been trying to figure out why they'd been abandoned before the area became overgrown.

"Depends on if it was just a local line that got shut down... or something bigger," Angie suggested. "It's probably just a side-route that no longer gets used and eventually connects to a main line."

Tall lanky Cam, pushed a stray lock behind her ear and grinned at her mom. She kept her hair trimmed short enough to mostly hide under her ever-present Mariners cap. "I saw you looking up railways on the internet last night. So what if it is something bigger?"

"If it's part of a bigger line out here, it might be part of the Milwaukee Road rail that shut down in the seventies. They had a line from Montana to here. One of the first lines over the Cascades."

"So, back when you were a kid?" Emma guessed.

Angie laughed. "A little before my time, but not by much. You can stop making me feel old now."

"Okay, so if it's part of that, what do you think is out here?" Cam pressed. The small group wandered further into the wilderness.

"More of the same, most likely. But there were often little junctions or yards. It's not like we're in the middle of nowhere. Just don't get your hopes up. There's a lot of abandoned tracks."

"Sure, but it's still cool to, you know, just go and see," Riley said. She drifted back closer to the group again.

The girls got quiet – looking around as they explored – following the tracks with sections partly torn up, a lot of the wood long since rotted away, and stretches simply too overgrown or damaged to find. But they always picked up on the trail again.

They'd move from seniors to ambassadors next year. With eleven years of scouting behind them none of the girls were strangers to the outdoors. By far, Cam found the trail, shortcuts, or easier routes the most often, but she also had a lot more hours at this. The running joke was the Walkers were well-named, and their unofficial family motto was, 'Let's go find out!'

Angie settled back into her usual pace. She kept an eye on them, making sure Riley's wandering, or Cam's daredevil moments didn't get them in too much trouble. But she let the girls choose the course and fell into step again each time the group moved forward.

Just as Emma called for a break, Riley – who had wandered ahead again – stopped just around a bend. "Whoa!"

"What is it?" called the out-of-breath Emma. She picked up her pace, trying to catch up.

"You guys have got to come see this!"

When they rounded a dense collection of trees, the group spotted the trio of old train cars Riley had found, all as worn down as the train tracks. Rusted links still hooked them together – the cars decorated in badly faded and chipped graffiti, plant growth, dirt, and the general weight of time.

"Neat!" said Cam and Emma in unison, exchanging a grin at the perfect timing.

"Just a minute, girls..." Angie dug a flashlight out of her hiking pack and moved closer. "Hello...hello," she called out. When there was no answer, she used the light to check under, around, and finally inside the cars that were open. The only residents turned out to be squirrels, so she waved the girls over. "You can look around. Just be careful, okay?"

The trio dashed in and investigated the train cars. Riley and Emma took pictures, and Cam quickly climbed up into the nearest one. "Geez, wonder how long these have been out here?" she shouted.

"Long enough for all these trees to grow through them. For stuff to rust out," Riley said. She put her phone away and headed to join Cam.

Cam helped Riley up, then did the same for Emma. Emma's height caused more trouble in reaching her, but at least she was lighter. And finally Cam offered her mother a hand up. Angie shined the flashlight so they all got a look around the car.

"Can I use the flashlight a minute?" Emma requested. Angie handed it over, and the girl completed a more detailed circuit of the train car.

"Looking for something?" Riley asked. "'Cause usually it'd be me or Cam needing to check every single thing out."

"Looking for signs of ghosts," said Emma. She turned around and grinned and held the flashlight under her chin, illuminating her face. "And before you tell me, 'that's ridiculous, 'cause this is a cargo car' – so? Haunted train stories are cool."

Cam blinked. "Haunted train stories?"

Emma rejoined the group and sat down in the train's dark interior, holding the flashlight like she was telling ghost stories at camp. The others hesitated a little, but after a bit of encouragement from Angie, they sat down too.

When everyone had settled in, Emma continued. "So, I'd kinda read the one about Lincoln's funeral train recently, in a collection of real ghost stories. And when Cam told me about these tracks, I just had to look up a few more... and found out there's lots."

"Okay, cool, but first, Lincoln's ghost train?" Riley said, nudging her with an elbow.

Emma nodded, kind of throwing off the effect of her light, but she couldn't help it. Ghost stories were her favorite. "So, April, 1865... after President Lincoln was killed, they put his body on a train and sent it on a long tour. People lined up to see it in lots of towns."

"Sure, that makes sense," Cam said.

"That's not it, though," Emma continued. "In a bunch of those towns, in places where tracks are – or especially where tracks used to be – people claim, on some nights in April, they can still hear the train whistle or see lights."

"Okay, that's kind of creepy," Riley said.

"You mean cool, right?" Emma said. "Besides, that's not remotely the only one. One of the coolest stories is up in St. Louis... not Missouri – St. Louis, Saskatchewan. Apparently Canada has one too. Anyway... people up there kept reporting hearing train whistles and seeing lights. And not just a couple of people or just recently. It's been going on for decades."

"Seriously?" Riley said.

Emma nodded again. "Lots of people. Like, enough that six years ago, Canada had a bunch of postage stamps come out with different legends, and the St. Louis Ghost Train was one of them."

"Okay, so maybe that's a little cool," Riley said.

"You want to hear an even better one?" Emma asked, grinning at Riley.

"Uhm, I guess so."

"Well, you're the one who reads all those mysteries and all. Want to hear about a ghost train murder mystery?"

Riley leaned forward. "Really?"

Emma grinned. "This one is out in Pennsylvania... dozens of people claimed they saw blue, floating lights near a place called Duffy's Cut."

"Okay, so what does that have to do with ghost trains and murder?" Riley said.

"Hold on, I'm getting to it. So, these lights were always at the same spot, right near the railroad tracks. And people spread the story they were ghosts of railway workers... The stories got so popular that a couple of people with ties to the railroad through their father, or their grandfather, or something... anyway, these guys decided to investigate. And here's where it really gets spooky..."

"Is there a postage stamp of them, too?" Riley wondered aloud.

"Maybe there should be," Emma said. "'Cause they actually managed to get some scientists from local universities involved. And eventually, they were able to dig near where the ghost lights kept appearing, and they found a mass grave."

Riley blinked. "Whoa, no way?"

"Way," Emma assured her. "Not only that, further investigation found the people had been shot. So that time, I guess you could kind of say the train worker ghosts were like detectives and helped people find the bodies."

Riley shivered. "Okay, that's... whoa... kinda insane."

Angie nodded. "Kind of. And maybe enough about ghosts

right now? At least until we're not in a dark train car in the middle of the woods?"

Riley was quiet for a moment, then reached for the flashlight. "How about different murders instead?"

Angie hesitated, then nodded. "She had her turn. What do you have in mind?"

Riley straightened up and displayed her best effort at the Belgian accent she'd heard on TV. "Well, everyone knows about Hercule Poirot, yes?" she asked. She mimed toying with one end of the famous detective's notable mustache. "And Agatha Christie's *Murder on the Orient Express*?"

"I guess, sure," Cam said. "Even I've heard of it."

Riley rolled her eyes. "Heard of one of the best mysteries ever written? With a victim who isn't what he seems, a dozen suspects, a train stuck in a snowbank... trapping everyone on board with a murderer... and a murderer who is either like one of Emma's ghosts, and snuck out a window with no other trace... or is one of the people... all of whom have alibis?"

"Okay, okay," Cam said. "So what happened? Who did it?"

Riley smiled bigger. "I'm not going to tell you that. You're going to have to read it for yourself. But what if I told you it was only one of bunches of mysteries set on trains?"

"So, people copying Christie?" Cam said.

Riley shook her head. "Even before her. Zola in the 1890's. Graham Greene wrote *Stamboul Train* a year before *Murder on the Orient Express.* Christie even went back to murder on a train in *4.50 from Paddington.*"

Cam couldn't help but tease. "So, that's about that teddy bear, right?"

Riley smirked. "It was one of Miss Marple's mysteries. One of the first great female detectives. A friend of Miss Marple's swears, that when she was on a train, passing another train going the opposite way, she saw a murder being committed. A man was strangling a blonde woman in a fur coat. Except when she reports it, the people on the other train can't even find a body."

"And you're still not going to tell me what happens, are you?" Cam said.

"Not a chance. But I am going to tell you that it only makes sense there'd be a lot of people writing murder mysteries on trains. It's a natural setting for it."

"Okay, how so?" Angie said.

"Well, for one thing, you have a bunch of people in a contained space." She gestures to the dimensions of the train car. "You can meet all of them pretty quickly, like reading off the passenger list. There's a limited number of places to hide things. So you know stuff like murder weapons are around there somewhere. And there's nowhere, really, for the killer to go."

"Seems like there's a time limit on solving it too," Emma said thoughtfully. "Because once the train stops, I guess you can try and detain people. But it seems like it's a lot harder."

"That too," Riley agreed.

"So what would be your murder mystery on a train?" Angie asked.

Riley straightened up again and looked all dignified. "Well, a lot of the best mysteries have three character types who are normally at the center of everything. Like, going back to Doyle's Holmes mysteries."

"Which are?" Angie asked.

"So obviously, you have the brilliant but quirky detective."

"Good start. Tell us about Detective Riley," Angie said with a hint of amusement.

"Detective Riley is, like, always three steps ahead of everyone else, thinking in puzzles, and seeing all the clues everyone else is overlooking, but..."

"But?" Emma said at the pause.

"But that's where she needs her brilliant assistant. See, in detective stories, a lot of the time, the detective needs a sidekick to deal with all those quirks. Holmes, Poirot, Wolfe – they all have someone to do things they can't and to help them relate to people."

"And Detective Riley's assistant is?" Angie said.

"Professor Emma. 'Cause Riley is always thinking three moves ahead, she needs someone who's super smart, so they can talk books and stuff, but who can keep track of what's going on right now. And she'd help Riley remember words and stuff, 'cause her head's always in the clouds."

"Sounds like a pretty good team. So what's this third person thing?" Cam asked.

"Well, if you bring in the great detective, you've got to have the cops baffled first. So there's usually, like, a police detective, or guy from Scotland Yard, but they're..."

Cam grinned. "But they're kinda dumb? At least compared to Detective Riley?"

Riley nodded sheepishly. "Kinda. I mean, they're often, like, really smart, and do their own thing well, but the detective comes in when it's weird stuff, so..."

Cam nodded. "Does that mean Inspector Cameron is, like, pretty smart, but not great at weirdness? But Detective Riley and Professor Emma still need her to run down the bad guy, punch their lights out, and haul them off after they've figured it all out?"

Riley brightened. "Yes! Yes, exactly. Inspector Cameron is a legit badass."

Angie laughed. "Nice save. So, Cam, honey, how about you? You have any favorite train stories?"

Cam nodded. "It's more a movie thing than a book thing, though. Not like Emma's ghost stories, or Riley's detectives."

"Movies are perfectly good stories too, honey. Let's hear it."

Cam nodded and stood. She moved around and gestured wildly as she tried to evoke the scene in her head. "So, those other stories are mostly passenger train stories. But there's some really cool stuff from cargo trains like the one we're on. Like train robberies!"

"Like, safes, and treasure, and bandits?" Riley asked.

"Exactly! I mean, whole towns depended on the railroad for supplies. Armies put payrolls on trains. A lot of American towns are where they are because trains stopped there, and there used to be a lot of competition between people trying to figure out where to put the railroads, because they were so important."

Angie's smile remained. "So are you the defender or the robber?"

"I mean, planning a heist seems like it could be pretty neat. But that seems more like a Riley thing, in the Old West. Nah, I'm the Lieutenant in charge of keeping the army payroll safe, when she finds out that bandits are going to attack the train!" Cam pointed finger guns out the open door of the car.

"Nuh uh!" Riley chimed in. "If this were my old west story, we'd all be planning the heist together. But no way am I being on the other side from you. 'Cause, number one, we stick together, right?"

Cam grinned and nodded. "So, number one. There's more?"

"Well, we just know if it involves running, climbing-around-on-a-train-action-scene stuff... probably shooting... you're gonna win. So we're with you, Lieutenant!"

"Okay, so you're all on the same team. Who are you?" Angie said.

"Oh yeah, huh... lemme think..."

Emma chimed in. "I'm the accountant."

Cam looked at her and blinked. "The accountant?"

"Well yeah, sure," Emma said. "If you have a payroll, you have to have someone who is good with money, too. And in the movies, that person is like, usually the plucky comic relief... and that's okay. Especially because they always get that one moment, after they've spent the movie just getting the best lines. They're still the comic relief, right up 'til almost the end. Then you find out – while the big heroes are fighting the obvious bad guys – they've snuck one or two people onto the train, or done something while there was a distraction... and that guy everyone was always laughing at, has a tiny gun or something, and manages to take out the bad guy that's right by the safe!"

"Oh yeah, neat!" Cam agreed.

"I will totally be your plucky comic relief. Just give me my fifteen seconds of fame with my tiny gun," Emma said.

"Sold," Cam agreed. Both looked to Riley.

Riley saluted Cam. "Sergeant, second-in-command is reporting, Ma'am. You do the punching, and running around, and jumping off the train onto a bandit's horse, and stuntman stuff. I'll be right here..." She laid down on her stomach in front of the door and mimed holding a rifle. "...sharp shooting bandits and stuff, with cover and a long-range weapon, like a sane person."

Cam grinned. "Sane, in an action-western?"

"You get that final fist-fight with the bandit leader on top of a moving train, Ma'am, but I betcha I get just as many train-robbers as you do, maybe more. And I'll do it from right here, and don't need a stunt double."

Cam snorted. "I do all my own stunts."

Angie sighed. "That's true, and you have the old x-rays to prove it."

Cam had the decency to blush, before turning around and sitting down with her mother again. "So how about you, Mom? Any train stories?"

"Okay, last one, then we need to head home before it starts getting dark," Angie said. "But I do. And my favorite stories were on trains exactly like this one."

The girls all settled in to listen.

"So, when I was a little girl, there were still stories of hobos – traveling workers who kind of followed the seasonal work. Not nearly so many stories as in earlier times... but still some. And it always sounded so fascinating."

"I hadn't heard about this," Cam said.

Angie smiled. "I guess it doesn't come up very much. But, sure... people who just... packed up what they could carry, hopped onto a train that was stopped or about to leave the station, and rode the rails to end up somewhere totally different. And when the work dried up, they'd pack up and move to the next town."

"Huh... I guess that kinda makes sense. That's why we do all of the hikes and everything. To go see something different?"

"Never thought of it quite like that, but that probably plays into it a little. Where I grew up, there were miles, and miles, and miles of fields. You had to really get out and go to see something different. Town was a thirty-minute drive. A city was a day trip. But you know, that probably influenced my desire to go see things... definitely inspired thoughts of jumping on a train every time I heard those whistles in the middle of the night. For some different scenery."

"So you actually put serious thought into it, sounds like?" Cam said.

"Thought, and some reading, even. There was a whole culture around it during the Depression and afterwards. Hobos would leave signs on the trains or along the rails for other hobos, about places to find work, food... or to warn each other of danger, like police who didn't like them much... just about anything. That was kind of the original graffiti I suppose... If you looked closely enough, and knew what to look for, you could find messages from people who'd traveled that way before."

Riley got up and shined the flashlight on the walls of the train car. She inspected them closely, as if she might find some tell-tale scratches.

Emma got up and joined her. "It'd be kind of like its own

ghost story if we found some... messages left for the people who come later."

Cam smiled at her mom. "So, what happens if I go home and mention that you wanted to be a hobo and wander the rails? Still ever think of just, you know, packing up and seeing what's out there?"

Angie leaned over and squeezed Cam with a one-armed hug. "All the time. But these days, those thoughts include my wife and daughter, and we just buy tickets. Seems a little easier and a lot safer. Speaking of which..."

"Okay, okay..." Riley wandered back and handed over the flashlight. "Time to get going. But... can we come back next weekend? I want to look around some more... and see if there's anything else further down the tracks."

Angie glanced at the trio and headed for the door of the train car. "Knowing you three... there will be."

Artist's Bio: Lesia Tiongson creates unique, heartfelt, and whimsical mosaic art. Her work consists of wide ranging designs and commonly features visually-contrasting elements on mediums of various substrates based on an eclectic mix of natural Pacific Northwest and manufactured materials.

Her work reflects a view of nature and human sentiment through a simple philosophy – everything has a shape.

These mosaic art pieces provide a unique tactile observation of nature through texture and three dimensions.

Though her art has found a nationwide audience, she is based in the small town of North Bend, WA, where she can be found teaching local workshops.

Author's Bio: Jeffrey Cook is an indie author living in Maple Valley, WA with his wife, housemate, and two large dogs. He's written 23 books with more on the way, mostly in the worlds of steampunk sci-fi, urban fantasy, and a bit of space opera.

Outside of writing, he's an avid gamer when he can manage the time, a regular attendee on the local convention circuit as vendor and panelist, and a sports fan when he has a free weekend.

In addition to working with FVP Books, he works with Clockwork Dragon, a Western Washington based indie author co-op, and he helped to found Writerpunk Press, a small charity press that writes science fiction adaptations to benefit PAWS Animal Rescue in Lynnwood, WA.

Photo: Tara Sreekumar, plentyopixels.com

HIDEOUT ⊗ Leslie Kreher

Leslie Kreher   David S. Moore

Leslie's Inspiration: I connected with animals and Nature in a profound way since my childhood. I believe that 'We are all One' and I hope that my artwork conveys how we are a part of Nature and not separate from it. Nature reflects beauty. It can connect us to the Infinite and to our authentic selves. I try to be true to my authenticity in my work.

Leslie's Partnership: As far as why I chose the image, David's story was about a 1820 era train hidden somewhere in the Pacific Northwest woods. After some research on what style trains were in use in that time period, I chose a steam train with a cow catcher surrounded in PNW fog. David and I collaborated with the general idea, but he won't see the final artwork until it's published.

David's Partnership: When David and Leslie first connected, he replied: It's interesting that you made it a steam train. That's exactly the type of train described in the story. Were you reading my mind while I wrote it? Hmmm... scary.

David's Inspiration: The topic of things lost implies mystery. I thought it would be interesting to see if I could compress a mysterious tale of a train lost in the forests of the Pacific Northwest into the confines of a 5,000 word story. I wanted the story to be engaging – something that would grab the reader from the start – and I also wanted it to have a satisfying, if somewhat macabre, ending. I hope I succeeded. :-)

THE SHANGHAIED TRAIN
MYSTERY
by David S. Moore

Clive Wooten stumbled into the deserted Wicked Witch Alehouse and took a seat at the bar.

"Hey, Mike – gimme a beer."

Mike poured a schooner and placed it in front of Clive.

"Thanks."

Clive quaffed his beer and signaled for another.

"What's the occasion?"

"I gots to steel myself. I'm sposed to meet a reporter."

"Reporter? What's a reporter want with you?"

Clive looked at him askance. "None 'o your business is what! Now pour me my beer!"

"Alright."

Mike refilled his schooner and Clive took a long draught. And as he set his glass down on the counter a man in his mid-thirties with T-shirt, leather jacket, jeans, beard, and long hair entered the bar. The man walked over to Clive's barstool and extended his hand.

"Are you Mr. Clive Wooten?"

Clive nodded but ignored the offered hand.

"I'm Jason Masters of the Valley Gazette."

"So you're the reporter what was askin' for me, right?"

"Yes Sir."

"C'mon, let's go over here..." Clive gestured to a booth in the far corner.

"So Mr. Wooten, what can you tell me about the lost train of gold?"

"Shhh! Not so loud. It's a story goes back to the war."

"Do you mean the Iraq war?"

"No, no! Way before that! The Second World War!"

"Oh, okay, okay."

"See there was these three miners in Montana – somewheres between Bozeman and Billings. And sometime around the early forties they struck a lode that was the biggest the state had ever seen!"

"Uh, do you know the name of their claim?"

"The Hidden Treasure Mine. That's what it was."

Jason made a note on his pad.

"Anyways it was right in the middle of the war, of course. And gold was one 'o them strategy minerals."

"Uh, I think you mean strategic materials."

"Right, right. Anyways the goverment controlled these minerals, see? And they didn't want nobody shipping them outside the country. So these miners – they was all Jacksons, they was brothers, see – they get this crazy idea that they'll sell their gold to the goverment for the goverment's dirt cheap price. But then once the gold was put on a train to go back east to some small town near Nashville – that's where the goverment wanted it shipped, see? Anyways these brothers – the Jacksons – they was going to hijack the train and ship the gold outta San Francisco to China where they had a buyer."

"So they were planning to sell the gold twice – once to the government and once to their fence."

Clive nodded. "Right! Purty clever, huh?"

Jason shrugged. "Don't know, wouldn't the police or the military just chase them down? I mean, how hard can it be to catch a hijacked train?"

"Well, that's where it gets innerestin'. The gold gets loaded onto a train in Montana and starts headin' towards Denver. But the Jackson brothers, they hijack the train just north 'o Cheyanne and they head west. And it's the middle of winter, see? And the snow is a-blowin', and the wind is a-howlin', and the cops – they can't keep up with the train 'cuz the roads they're just like ice. So the Jacksons, they drive this train all the way to Washington State and then head south toward San Francisco on an old freight line that was mostly used by lumber mills. But then something happened somewhere and nobody ever saw the train again."

"Huh. So the Jackson brothers didn't make it to San Francisco."

Clive shrugged. "Nobody knows fer sure. But one story says the feds was on their tail so they ran the train up an ol' logging line and hid out there. But the weather turned really nasty – bitter cold – and they all froze. And so that train and all that gold – it's probly on an ol' spur somewheres right here in this valley!"

Jason stood up. "Well, thank you Mr. Wooten for that very entertaining story."

"Hey, wait! You said you'd give me a hundred dollars!"

"I said I'd give you a hundred dollars for a useful lead on the lost train of gold. But all you've given me is a decades old fairy tale that I can't follow up on! Where are the Jackson brothers now? Oh, that was so long ago they're probably all dead! And nobody knows whether they made it to San Francisco, or if they died of frostbite in the wilds of Washington State! And all that gold – did any of it ever make it to China? Well, we'll never know because nobody knows where the train is! Now that's a story with lots of intrigue and fascination – could make a great movie, maybe. But no one will ever find that train or any of the gold because there's not one useful clue in the entire yarn!"

"But..."

"Here, buy yourself another beer." Jason put a five-dollar bill on the table and left the Wicked Witch. And after he had left, Clive took the bill and tucked it in his wallet.

Jason Masters walked the main street of the Podunk town that was home to the Wicked Witch Alehouse and found the disheveled office of the Valley Gazette.

"May I help you sir?" asked the man behind the counter.

"Hi, I'm Jason Masters. I'm researching the history of this fair region for a book I'm writing."

"Oh?" The man rose from his desk. "What sort of book?"

"It's about how this region weathered the Great Depression and how it supported and recovered from World War II."

"Oh, very interesting! Say, I'm George Willis." He extended his hand and Jason shook it. "Did you know that this valley once had the largest hops farm in the world?"

"Is that right? So listen, I was wondering if I could look at some of your old records."

"Sure, come on back." He escorted Jason to a room stacked with cupboards. George opened one and revealed reels of microfilm. "Help yourself. The reader's in that corner, and each of these cabinets is labeled with the years they cover."

"Hey, thanks. This is perfect. Listen, George, it might take me a couple of hours. Will that be okay?"

"Sure, no problem! We close at five. Just make sure you put everything back where you found it."

"Sure thing."

Later that evening Jason flopped onto the bed of his motel room and reviewed the day's results. Clive Wooten repeated almost verbatim the story he'd heard from a hundred other narrators. The brothers Jackson, operators of The Hidden Treasure Mine, sold some gold to the U.S. government during World War II. The news reports he'd read over the years said they sold the equivalent of about ten bars of gold. On the open market that would have been worth more than $2 million at the time. But because the Gold Reserve Act was in force the Government would only pay $35 an ounce, making their entire shipment worth less than $150,000. So they hijacked the train onto which the gold had been loaded, and drove it west in a snowstorm to Washington State. They turned south on a freight line – that was chiefly used for logging – to head south toward San Francisco. From there they planned to ship it to a buyer somewhere in China.

But something went wrong. The snow forced them to pull off onto a spur somewhere in the forests. Or they tried to hide from the feds by following an old line deep into the woods and eventually froze to death. Or a band of marauding Sasquatch boarded the train and carried them off deep into the forest to be served as the main course of a tribal feast.

But that was only part of the story. Miners from several Montana mines had sold their ore to the government, and not all of it was gold. There was nickel, chromium, titanium – all of which were considered more essential materials than gold for the war effort.

The brothers Jackson hijacked the train on December 19th, 1942. His research at the Gazette proved the winter of 1942 was especially cold, with several feet of snow recorded in higher elevations around the valley on December 20th. So it was indeed possible that snow brought the hijackers' devious plan to a frigid end.

But more importantly he'd found a reference to Melissa Stevens, reputedly the granddaughter of Burt Jackson, in a back issue of the Valley Gazette. After hours of digging he found an article about her wedding in 2002 to a Mr. Robert Stevens, proprietor of a used car dealership somewhere in the very valley that was once home to the largest hops farm in the world.

Jason ate the last piece of pizza, then finished his beer. Tomorrow he would spend tracking down Mrs. Stevens to see if she could add any details to a legend he'd been researching for the previous ten years.

"Coming!" said Mrs. Melissa Stevens in response to a knock at her front door. She opened it to find a bearded man, maybe mid-thirties and not bad looking. "Yes?"

"Good afternoon, Ma'am. Are you Mrs. Stevens?"

"Yes."

"I'm Jason Masters of the Washington State Historical Society."

"Oh?"

"Yes, Ma'am. I'm doing some research on the history of the Northwest."

"So? What's that got to do with me?"

"I saw you and your father in your wedding photograph."

"Really. Where did you see that?"

"The Valley Gazette archives."

"Oh, yeah. That's right. We sent them a copy and I couldn't believe they printed it. They must not have had much else to report that day."

"It must have been a lovely wedding. Your father looked very dapper in his tuxedo."

"Yes, didn't he though? I think it was the proudest moment of his life. Why don't you come inside?" She led him to a small living room with a couch, a coffee table, and children's toys scattered all over.

"Nice house you have here, Mrs. Stevens."

"Why, thank you. Would you like some tea?"

"That would be wonderful."

She disappeared into the kitchen to prepare the tea and Jason took the occasion to examine the photos arrayed on her mantle.

"Your wedding dress was beautiful," Jason said when she returned. "Did you make it yourself?"

She shook her head. "Oh, no. I'm not that talented. That was all my mother's doing."

"So she was a seamstress?"

"Well, she didn't do it for a living. But she could sew just about anything. Dresses, blouses, shirts... I've still got a dozen napkins and placemats she sewed for me as a wedding present."

Jason pointed to one of the pictures on the mantle. "This photo – is that your father?"

"Uh huh."

"Was his name Christian Jackson?"

"Why, yes! My, you are quite the historian, aren't you!"

"And wasn't he the son of Burt Jackson?"

She stood still and her eyes turned cold. "Is this about that stupid train? Is that why you're here?"

He nodded. "Yes, Ma'am. I just thought you might..."

"You thought I might be able to lead you to a train that's

been lost somewhere in the miles and miles of forests around here – a train that's chock full of gold! Well let me tell you something mister; my grandfather worked that stupid mine for thirty years. He never even knew my father! He left my grandmother before my father was born and went off to work the mine with his brothers and he never came back! So he never told my father or anybody else anything about that stupid train!"

Tears welled in her eyes. She reached for a tissue and dabbed them dry.

"It must have been very hard on your father."

"It was hard on everyone! But especially my father. He never had time for school because he had to work from when he was fifteen years old." She plopped down on the couch and sobbed.

A boy, maybe five years old, entered the living room. Melissa quickly dabbed at her cheeks again as he climbed onto the couch and handed her a book.

"Jaime, why don't you take your train to your room? We have a guest and Mommy needs to talk to him. Okay?"

"Oh, all right." He took his train up the stairs.

"He seems like a pretty good kid."

She nodded. "Yes, he is. He's my little hero."

"Well, listen Mrs. Stevens, the tea was wonderful, and I've already wasted enough of your time. You've told me everything I need to know. You never saw your grandfather after the robbery, and you don't know what happened to him or to either of his brothers. So..." He stood up. "I should be going."

"Before you do, Mr. Masters..." She got up and went to a

back room. She returned with a framed photograph and handed it to him. It showed four men standing at a bar.

"That's your grandfather," he said, pointing to one of the men.

"Yes. And his two brothers – Brad and Bryan."

"Who's the fourth man?"

She shook her head. "I don't know."

"Would your father know?"

"He passed away five years ago."

"Oh, I'm so sorry, Mrs. Stevens."

"Don't be. He was a good man. He worked hard all his life. But he had a good life, and people who loved him. So…" She wiped her nose. "So he died content."

"Well, that's all that matters, isn't it?"

She nodded.

"Well, thank you so much Mrs. Stevens. I really appreciate your time."

"Why don't you keep that picture, Mr. Masters? I don't really want it around here anymore. It just brings back bad memories of that stupid train."

"Are you sure?"

She wiped her nose again, then nodded. "Yes. I'm sure."

Jason drove to a nearby park, sat at a picnic table, took the photo out of its frame and scanned it into his notepad. He studied the image. All four of the men were wearing coveralls; none wore a hat; all were bearded. There was nothing distinctive about the bar itself – it could have been almost anywhere. But one thing he saw seemed important. When he zoomed in, he could clearly see that the fourth man's shirt bore the logo of... The Milwaukee Road!

So maybe this fourth man was an employee – or former employee – of the railroad. And maybe this fourth man provided the inside information necessary to help the Jackson brothers elude the police and the feds on their several-hundred-mile sojourn across the northwest.

Ten years he'd studied this heist. He'd questioned dozens of people between Billings and Seattle about it. Evenings, weekends, vacations – all his spare time had been devoted to solving a mystery that might never be solved. But now – here in a photograph that Mrs. Stevens was only too eager to rid herself of – he had his first substantively new clue in the last five years.

But what could he do with it? Suppose this fourth man was indeed an employee of the railroad. What information could he provide a band of thieves who wanted to commandeer a train?

Two facts about the hijacking never made much sense to him. According to news reports at the time, the Jacksons hijacked the train on the northern outskirts of Cheyenne and then headed west. That's how everyone he had ever talked to about the heist had described it. The problem is, they would have had to go all the way into Cheyenne before they could've turned west. There just weren't any westbound lines north of the city. And that always seemed too risky.

But what if they'd hijacked the train after it had left Cheyenne? That possibility had seemed unlikely to him because a team of miners wouldn't know the best route by which to head west. They wouldn't know that with a little backtracking they could hop on an old line that meandered through the southern reaches of Laramie County, Wyoming, before merging with the main line in Albany County, near US 287 – and that doing so would be the fastest way to lose anyone trying to track them down in a car. With the help of someone who knew the railroad lines well, they could have found their way to that obscure line through the back country. Yes, the snow helped. But an experienced railroad worker would have known the best route to take to lose the police and the feds.

Another problem: Why did they turn north? The news reports – and every account he'd ever heard – said the train went north into Washington State. Why go over the Rockies, then over the Cascades into Western Washington? San Francisco is almost due west of Cheyenne. Going through Washington State would have added hundreds of unnecessary miles.

But again, if they had someone who knew the railroads, maybe they did it for a reason. Maybe their plan was to run the train up an old logging line deep in the forests of Washington State, then hide it somewhere in the mountains on a forgotten spur. Then they'd disappear for a time – months, or even years – and eventually they'd go back and drive the train out of its hiding place to San Francisco. And to do that you would want someone who knows where you could hide a train for months – or years – without anyone finding it.

So, if he could think like a railroad worker, maybe he could figure out where they took the train, and where they hid it. After a little digging he found online maps of railroad lines that showed both existing and abandoned track. And after studying maps of the region for most of the afternoon he concluded there was only one viable possibility. They would've had to turn northeast prior to reaching Kennewick, Washington, then turn west before reaching Spokane. At what's now the city of Monroe they would've turned south on a now-abandoned line that would've taken them into logging country. From there a number of lines turned off into the depths of the forests.

There was one abandoned segment of railroad that especially interested him. The online map showed a stretch of track no more than a mile long, just north of a small lake deep in the forest. The map showed nothing – not even a logging road – to connect that stretch of track to any other line. It was just out there by itself in the middle of the forest.

The markings on the map indicated the area around the lake was swampy. Or maybe a bog. There were no nearby towns, and the nearest railroad line was at least three miles distant. The only nearby roads were built long after the war.

A bog. What if the railroad had built a line out to that remote site to support the loggers, and they discovered too late that the land around was so boggy their track simply sank into the earth under the weight of a fully loaded train? That would explain why the Jackson brothers were never able to get their shipment to San Francisco. Tomorrow – the last day of his vacation – he would have to hike out there to see for himself.

The next morning Jason made some coffee and reread the letter that had set him on the trail of the Jackson brothers ten years earlier. It was one of many papers he found when his mother Irene died of lung cancer.

Dearest Roberta,

You know my brother's and me been working this mine for years. And you been wondering when we're going to see results. Well we struck a major lode and we'll be selling some gold soon. The government don't pay much but we got a special buyer in China. And when we sell it I'm taking my share and you and me and Irene, we're moving to San Francisco. I know that's where you always wanted to live. We'll get a big house on Nob Hill with a nice kitchen. I know how much you've wanted a nice kitchen. Anyways it won't be much longer. So keep the faith and remember that I love you always.

Brad

He also found his mother's marriage license, which listed her maiden name as Jackson. So his mother, Irene Jackson, was the daughter of Brad Jackson who had been working a gold mine with his brothers for years. And they were planning to sell the gold from their mine to a buyer in China soon after the letter was written – December 2nd 1942. It wasn't too hard to find write-ups in newspapers from the time about a train filled with ore that was hijacked near Cheyenne on December 19th. And even though the perpetrators were not identified, he knew that one of them was his own grandfather – Brad Jackson!

So he had known for the last 10 years that the essential outline of the story was true. The Jackson brothers were indeed planning to sell some ore to a buyer in China. And the sale was scheduled to happen shortly after December 2nd. He knew the story had more than just a kernel of truth. And that meant that somewhere in the forests of Washington State there was a train loaded with gold that was rightfully his family heritage. He just had to find it.

He packed a lunch, took a water bottle, put on his hiking boots, sunglasses, a hat, and got in his rented car. He took the old logging road that ran closest to the lake and parked just north of it behind some trees. It would still be a five mile hike to the lake.

The land was indeed quite boggy. His boots sank down a couple of inches into the muck, and with each step a slurping suction pulled at them. In half an hour he was sweating and his legs were tired.

A mile or so in he intercepted some railroad tracks partially submerged in the mud. The tracks ran north-south, and further north they must have spurred off from the main logging line. He followed the tracks south, toward the lake.

He came to another spur. This one headed east – away from the lake. He decided to follow it. The soil was still boggy, but as he headed further into the forest the track gained in elevation and the soil dried out. Soon the train tracks were no longer covered in muck and he could walk on the railroad ties. He hiked into thicker and darker forest. And then – through the underbrush he could just make out a mechanical shape on the tracks – a locomotive!

He fought his way through the salal and ferns. The train had been deliberately concealed with camouflage netting. No wonder the dozens of drones that had flown over the region had never found anything.

It was a steam locomotive with a coal car and two cargo cars. The locomotive was rusted, though otherwise undamaged. Getting it running again after more than 90 years would be a problem. The coal car was a bit less than half full, so at least there was plenty of fuel.

He pulled open the door of the first cargo car and climbed inside. His eyes fixed immediately on a safe that had been blown open. He reached inside, and...

"Nothing!"

Whatever gold or other precious metals were on board the train would have been in the safe. Someone – or several someones – had blown the safe and taken the gold. They must have carried it out of the forest on foot.

There were seven open bins on board, each filled with ore – five marked 'Nickel', and two 'Chromium'. Just as Clive had said, strategy minerals. Each bin probably weighed a ton or more – no way to carry those out of the forest.

In one corner of the car he saw something that looked like a rotting boot. But as he got closer, he realized the bones of a foot were still inside it.

What had happened? Both the tibia and fibula had been shattered – most likely by a shotgun blast. And on the wall of the car, just above the boot, was a streak of ruddy brown – blood? Another streak of ruddy brown ran across the car's floorboards from the boot to the door of the car.

There were more splotches of ruddy brown on the interior wall of the car, and holes in the wood – the kind of holes a shotgun would make.

So maybe there had been a gunfight. Or an ambush. And what about the person whose foot was blown off? Maybe the body was dragged out of the car. And then where?

He got out of the car and studied the surrounding terrain. Plenty of places to hide bodies. But why hide them?

"They purposefully hid the train," he reminded himself. "They hid it so they could return at some time in the future to drive the train out of the forest and take it to port."

It would be most unfortunate if a longshoreman were to discover dead bodies in the car as he unloaded its bins of strategic materials. The killer – or killers – must have dragged the bodies out of the car and away from the train.

"So the bodies would not have been hidden," he surmised.

He took a dozen steps into the forest – and found a heap of bones, rotted clothing, and five rotting boots underneath a growth of salal.

"Three bodies. One killer."

He headed back to the train to inspect the second cargo car. He pulled the door open and saw a dozen more open bins filled with ore, all marked, 'PROPERTY U.S. GOVERNMENT'. But before he could climb into the car for a closer look, he heard a voice.

"I wouldn't get in there if I were you, Mr. Masters."

He turned around and saw a man with a gun trained on him.

"Uh, who are you? How'd you get here?"

"I'm detective Steven Langford of the FBI. I've been following you for the last week."

"Oh?"

"We've had our eyes on you for some time, Mr. Masters. We were hoping you'd find some clue that would lead you to the train."

"So I did your work for you."

He shrugged. "Well, you solved a mystery that no one else was able to figure out in more than 90 years. For that, and on behalf of the bureau, I thank you." He lowered his gun.

"So what's in these bins?"

"The ore in that car is unprocessed uranium. In 1942 they

weren't terribly concerned about the hazards of radiation to human health. Besides, there was no radioactivity warning symbol at that time. Hence the lack of markings."

"Uranium? Where was it headed?"

"Building K-25 in Oak Ridge, Tennessee. That ore was supposed to be shipped to the Manhattan Project."

Jason smacked his forehead. "So the Jacksons' gold was loaded onto a train that was supposed to take uranium ore to a secret government project – one the Jackson brothers knew nothing about! And they hijacked the train to steal their own gold back from the government without realizing that they were threatening a project crucial to defeating the Germans."

"Yup. This train was deemed critical to the war effort and the government was very eager to find it. But the robbers got lucky. The snowstorm provided plenty of cover. Plus, they took a route heading west out of Cheyenne that made it almost impossible for the police to track them down."

"So they made it out here to the wilds of Washington State," Jason continued. "They hid the train. And the plan was to come back months or years later to drive the train out of the forest to San Francisco."

Langford nodded. "But apparently one of them got greedy. Looks like he killed the other three, blew open the safe, and took all the gold for himself."

"And by the time he returned to drive the train out of the woods the tracks in the surrounding bog had sunk below the surface. So he couldn't drive it out anyway."

"Right."

"So there's three bodies piled up in the woods 25 feet from the train. I have a photo that shows the Jackson brothers with a fourth man wearing coveralls with a Milwaukee Road logo."

Jason showed him the photo.

"Do you have any idea who that fourth man is?"

"Robert Chrisholm," Langford said. "He was the engineer on the train the day it was hijacked. He went missing that day and was never seen again."

"Ah, so the Jackson brothers had help."

"Sure did. Chrisholm was a railroad engineer for more than 30 years. He rode just about every inch of track between here and Chicago. We have no idea what happened to him. He just disappeared. Not even his wife of 35 years knew where he went."

Jason shrugged. "So what happens now?"

"That ore belongs to the government. So we'll bring in some heavy equipment and haul it away."

"What about the bodies?"

"In the eyes of the government they're all criminals. It's too late to prosecute them, and we already know we'll never find the gold."

"I'd like to think that the killer wasn't a Jackson. But if so, then one of the bodies is my grandfather's."

"If you want to research that possibility, we can let you do so – after the ore has been removed from the site."

"OK, fair enough. What about me?"

"Curiosity isn't a crime, Mr. Masters. And you haven't removed anything of value from the site. So as far as I'm concerned, you're free to go."

Jason surveyed the scene once again. "I can't believe I led

you right to it. But I guess I'm happy I found it, after all this time. At least I know what happened. Well, most of it anyway." He sighed. "Nice meeting you, Detective Langford."

"My pleasure Mr. Masters."

Artist's Bio: Leslie grew up in the Midwest drawing and painting. Her love of animals, especially horses, is part of her inspiration. Her creative spirit and love of nature shows in her career choices and she has been involved in marketing, owned a design business and managed a plant nursery. Between career and raising a family she continued to paint and study privately.

Since her move to Washington State in 2013, she has been lucky enough to call herself a "real full time artist." Leslie enjoys playing with different media, but her focus is on detailed graphite drawings and watercolor. Her profound connection with the Earth, Nature and animals inspires her to share the awesome beauty she feels through her art.

Leslie lives in Monroe, Washington with her artist husband Jeff Sturgeon, Dixie the dog and Cleo the cat. She is the President of the Mt. Si Artist Guild in the Snoqualmie Valley, helped to create their "Art Gallery of SnoValley" in Snoqualmie, and displays her work in venues around the Valley and beyond. In her spare time she rows competitive Crew with Sammamish Rowing and keeps a big garden.

Author's Bio: David S. Moore is a retired software engineer and architect. He is now pursuing his lifelong passion for writing. He has self-published the five volumes of a science fiction series titled *Mind Space* and a non-fiction book on religion titled *The Reverent Atheist*.

VANPORT FLOOD BEGINS ON COLUMBIA
RIVER MAY 30, 1948

⊗

Gayll Morrison

Gayll Morrison   Casondra Brewster

Gayll's Inspiration: The image I submitted for *The Lost Train Anthology* is from an original oil on canvas painting I did with the long event-descriptive title 'Vanport Flood begins on Columbia River on May 30, 1948'. This painting is a compilation of several old photographs from the historical event; a train trestle, a flooded farm, and the Columbia river overflowing its banks (pre flood control dams). Train travel was severely impacted and many trains were temporarily 'lost' in Oregon, Washington and British Columbia for quite some time I imagine. The original oil painting was in color but since the anthology was to be printed in black and white I converted the image to a grey scale and I really like the resulting black and white image as the overall tone and mood is much more in line with the original photographs.

Gayll's Partnership: Work completed before contact with author.

Casondra's Partnership: When viewing my artist's work in the context of juxtaposition of my story, the image spoke perfectly with me. No further collaboration was necessary and the fabulous artist, Gayll Morrison, agreed. Life is great when you're in sync.

Casondra's Inspiration: Immediately when thinking on this theme, the phrase lost train of thought popped into my head. Worries over memory loss as we age is something always in the forefront of my mind, as my spouse tends to be often like an absent-minded professor. Both of us struggle with recalling things, with how fast our modern life seemingly speeds. Additionally, we both have family members who passed due to dementia and Alzheimer's. Then there is this pandemic that we're living under at the time this story was authored. It's a time of great collective trauma. Trauma often makes us forget things – purposefully or just in a method of survival. People are often living within their own train of trauma and can become lost. And this is where Diane's story began.

AT A LOSS
DARK SPECULATIVE FICTION
by Casondra Brewster

It was there on the tip of her tongue, perched precariously between a quip and a stutter. Diane sat on a bench waiting for the commuter train, concentrating, grasping for recall. But as hard as she wanted the thought to come, it just evaporated. To where, she couldn't be certain.

Perhaps this is 'Pregnant Brain?' It was probably the rush to get here. She was running later than she liked to get to her appointment. That's why she felt all frazzled. She took a deep breath and forced a smile. *It's hard to feel sad if you make yourself smile.*

A decade ago she doubted she would find love again, let alone that it would grow into a little family. *Unbelievable.* She touched her belly, barely a baby bump now, and smiled involuntarily.

The train squeaked to a stop and Diane boarded. She found a seat quickly. There were few people getting on at her stop and she was glad to be moving toward downtown.

"Zone Pass," Diane lifted her chin so that the transit conductor could scan her eye. She was one of the few that could move about unencumbered by protective equipment. The scan would have told the transit worker that she was one of the 'immune' and that she was in compliance. She understood they had to do their jobs, but it felt invasive and bothersome, especially when she felt so hurried. Sometimes she wore a mask, just so people wouldn't stare at her. But today she was joyful and happy and didn't want it dampened by a stupid mask and gloves.

As the transit conductor moved on, Diane put her sunglasses on to protect her blue eyes. The sky was cloudy, but it was a weird light that hurt her eyes. She also didn't want anyone to know if she was looking at them. A woman seated kitty-corner from Diane in the seats nearest the door of the train car stared at her from behind a face mask. *People always stare at me.* Diane dug in her small bag for a mirror and finger-combed her black hair. Grooming complete, she looked out the window.

The I-5 corridor blinked by as the train got to its cruising speed. That brilliant green spattered against the pumice stone gray sky. Looking at it thrilled and depressed her all at once. But this was home. To leave it would be to run from everything she had always wanted. Besides it was almost the end of April, soon there would be gorgeous sunny days. And after summer, her family would be complete.

Just fifteen years ago, she wouldn't have believed you if

you told her she would be pregnant and happy about it. Fantasy and bald speculation! That would have been the past Diane's cry to her current self. She had first of all had zero luck with partners and the doctors always believed she would not be able to carry a child because of history of miscarriages. Here she was, a miracle of miracles. Yet three half-decades and her life had changed so drastically. Mostly for the good, except...

Except for something she couldn't even completely think about or articulate, it was just suspended in her brain, caught in her thought.

Why can't I remember? Maybe I should have brought a mask?

Masks. One item was such a controversy even all these years since this new virus came into the world. Diane looked towards the woman across from her momentarily and then thought back to her last appointment. Diane's doctor told her many women who became pregnant, even if they were immune, chose to wear a mask, because there was no certainty that her child would also be immune.

"Out of the four billion people who remain after this pathogen's appearance in our world," Dr. Robin Case said to Diane in their last appointment. *She's so dramatic.* Regardless, Diane did recall with much detail the speech she'd been given by Dr. Case. "Only a small percentage are immune like you – a non-carrier immune. Even though the father is also a non-carrier immune, you can't know for certain until well after 24 weeks if your baby is, and that testing is not even reliable. We won't know for sure, as the research shows, until the child is six years old. I would counsel you and the father to behave as if you are not immune." Diane had nodded in agreement but didn't feel it in her heart.

A brief wave of weariness came over her as the train crossed Lake Washington. She chalked it up to a poor night's sleep and then oversleeping and running late. Nightmares of contagion and riots in the street had awoken her early that day and she was prepared for a day of low energy and not feeling like making the journey into the doctor's office. She originally thought she should call and reschedule the appointment. After starting her day, listening to the birdsong as she sipped coffee on her patio, the nightmares faded, and Diane was excited for her appointment and her future in general. Hope for normalcy in her life and a life surrounded by family and friends gave her the boost she needed. Even if that boost came a half hour later than she needed.

Her view from the train window showed few people on the streets in the downtown area. The entire region had changed drastically in the last three years since The Rock Pox Virus had taken hold. That change was stark in the former bustling downtown. She was fine with lower populations being out and about. She felt less attacked when there were fewer people. The higher the population, the higher the chance of yet another person calling her unpatriotic, even when she explained she was immune. "Privileged Pollyanna!" they would yell. "Must be nice for you!" It made her feel bad. She was tired of feeling bad. She wasn't going to let anyone make her feel bad anymore. People used to praise folks who had good breeding. Not so much now. *I can't help it if I'm genetically superior.*

As the train made its way up Cherry Hill, Diane paid closer attention so she didn't miss her stop. She couldn't be any later. Letting her mind wander, always got her in trouble.

Trouble. There's always trouble.

As she departed the train, Diane avoided looking at the

woman who had stared at her earlier. The hospital was a two-block walk from the station and a gentle breeze blew, alluding to summer's approach.

She endured the security scan situated in what used to be a gorgeous welcoming hospital lobby. Now it was full of beeping machines, uniformed and masked people and this weird long snaking line made to keep people six feet apart. The process included another retinal scan to prove her immunity status.

This is why she wanted to arrive much earlier for her appointment. Sometimes this clearance took longer than it should. *Especially for someone who is immune, we should have a separate entrance.* She sighed heavily but moved through to the two medical stations.

The first one took her temperature. 97.9 degrees F. She was cleared to pass to the next one, which she didn't care for at all. This one was a bit larger than the last. A whirring black cover lowered down while the procedure went on, so its light didn't hurt anyone. It also stuck a full mask onto your face to protect your eyes. It gave the occupant an ultra-sonic and UV-light bath which killed many contagions. The jury was out on whether or not it was effective; but the greater Seattle area had taken to using every weapon in its arsenal against this current disease. *Really, if I'm immune, I shouldn't have to go through all this.* The process took way longer than a temperature and retinal scan and it made Diane feel claustrophobic and anxious. She tried to focus on her breath while the machine whirred around her in her temporary darkness. She diverted her thoughts to the baby in her belly to pass the time more quickly. She received the green light through the sanitizer station at last, and headed to the elevator to Dr. Case's office.

She approached the receptionist, who was encased in a

glass structure. Diane still felt it was odd for the receptionist to also wear a surgical mask, gloves, and a full-body apron over her street clothes. "Hello," the woman said to Diane. "How may I help you?"

"Diane Osman. I have a one o'clock appointment with Dr. Case," she looked around and there didn't seem to be any other patients about.

"Oh," the receptionist looked at her screen and then up at Diane, "Dr. Case isn't seeing patients today. Are you sure your appointment was today?"

"I'm certain of it," Diane said and looked at the clock on the wall above the receptionist's head. It read 12:56 p.m. "I'm a little bit late, but still before my appointment time. I'm certain."

"Alright, let me call someone; please have a seat in the yellow chair there, and I'll call you shortly."

A line of chairs stood watch behind Diane, against the wall that faced the receptionist's desk. They boasted rainbow colors with a black chair in between all of them. A woman, a bit younger than herself, sat in the purple chair. Funny enough she wore a purple face mask. Diane had not seen her come in. *She wasn't there when I came in. Maybe she's waiting for someone?* Diane took her place in the yellow chair.

The thought she was forgetting something haunted her. But she was certain her OB/GYN appointment was right now. She dug through her purse, because she remembered asking for an appointment card. They were reluctant to give her one because of the virus epidemic. She remembered showing it to her husband. She put it in her calendar. She was certain. *Where is that card?*

The receptionist hung up the receiver. "Ms. Robles?" The

woman in the purple chair got up. Diane watched and thought the woman looked familiar with dark hair and light eyes. The receptionist handed the woman some paperwork and the woman sat back down in the purple chair and began filling it out. *She doesn't look pregnant.* Diane dallied in her recollection that she hadn't looked pregnant the first time she came here either. She smiled at the woman, but the woman didn't see Diane's smile. She was focused on her paperwork.

A woman in blue scrubs with bright artwork of suns dotted all over them came out from the door opposite where patients would go in. She wore gloves and a surgical mask. She held a red folder. "Mrs. Osman?" she called.

"That's me," Diane said cheerily.

"Hi, I'm Nurse Monico. Please follow me."

Diane followed. The nurse brought her into a cubicle labeled, 'Vitals.' Diane took off her coat and folded it in her lap as she sat next to the desk.

The nurse pulled a temperature reader from her pocket and rubbed it over Diane's forehead.

"They just took my temperature when I came in," Diane said. "I'm certain I didn't get a fever in five minutes."

"Security has a different system. We do our own readings. It's important," Nurse Monico said. And she noted Diane's temperature on a tablet on the desk. She put an old-school blood pressure cuff on Diane's arm and pumped it up to gauge her blood pressure and heart rate. *I don't like this part.*

"Haven't they come up with a better way to take blood pressure yet?" Diane said, a note of impatience in her voice.

"I'll be quick, just be still and breathe normally please." Nurse Monico kept to her task.

Diane counted in her head and wiggled her toes to think about something other than the pressure on her upper arm. By the time she got to 30, the nurse had the cuff off and was noting the results on her tablet.

"Alright," the nurse said. "I *need* you to be honest with me. I have a series of questions to ask and I need you to be truthful."

"I don't lie," Diane said and put a hand to her chest.

"Well good, then this shouldn't be a problem."

Diane nodded.

"Alright, first question: Have you been having any problems with bleeding or spotting?"

"Oh, goodness, no," Diane fanned herself. "It is however, rather warm in here."

"I'll try to get you through this quickly," the nurse said. "Question two: Have you been taking your antibiotics?"

"You mean my prenatal vitamins?" Diane shot Nurse Monico a frown.

"You don't need to take prenatal vitamins," Nurse Monico said, her brow furrowed in confusion.

"Why not? Because of my immunity?"

"I mean, you could, if you like, it won't hurt you; but you don't need them anymore."

Diane touched her belly and looked up at the nurse, "Why wouldn't I take the vitamins? I want the best for my baby."

"Mrs. Osman, you do realize you are here for a follow-up appointment after your..." the nurse paused.

"My what?" Diane said.

"Mrs. Osman, two weeks ago today you were released from the hospital following a miscarriage."

"This is not funny!" Diane's mouth opened in a silent scream. But that silence lasted only a moment. Diane screeched, "You must have me mistaken for someone else!" She stood throwing her coat to the floor. As she did, a small white and gray something fell out and emitted a clacking noise at the nurse's feet.

Nurse Monico scooped to pick it up. She read the words aloud, "Saint Birgitta's Women's Hospital." She presented it to Diane Osman. "See, this was your admittance bracelet."

"I've never seen that before in my life." Diane took a step back. Nurse Monico still held out the clipped bracelet. "Why are you being so cruel?" Diane gasped and fainted.

Diane loved brilliant spring days like this – summer was just a month away and the day was promising to be very summer-like. She sat on the train headed to her doctor's. Today she wore a mask because she didn't feel like getting the odd stares from people for being immune to the Rock Pox Virus. The transit conductor who she hadn't seen in a while showed scars on his face. Those were a telltale sign of the disease. She was glad he was better. *I should say something to him.*

Diane smoothed her dress, the maternity sundress she had been dying to wear. She hoped Dr. Case wouldn't be so rushed today and would see her. There was something else she needed to talk to the doctor about, but she couldn't remember. *The test for the baby's immunity?* Hopefully it would come to her before she got to the hospital.

"Zone Pass," the fare enforcement officer stood above

Diane. He was a burly man with a gray mustache. Diane took off her sunglasses so he could do his scan.

"Thank you," he said to Diane. "It's good to see you again, Ms. Osman."

"Er, thank you," Diane muffled through her face mask. *How does he know me?*

The ride seemed to go faster than normal, and with the sun out, there were many more people downtown than the last time she went to the doctor. *When was that?*

She went through the security check, got her temperature taken and then moved forward to the sanitizing station. As she emerged from the black and glass contraption, she saw a woman coming out of the elevators. The woman wore blue scrubs with brilliant suns all over them. *I know that woman, I think.* The woman wore a surgical mask. Her hair was in a surgical cap.

"Mrs. Osman," the woman spoke.

Oh no, I can't remember her name.

Diane smiled with her eyes, aware she had her mask on today, and tried to move past the woman to take the elevator.

"What are you doing here?" the woman moved in front of Diane.

"I don't think it's any business of yours," Diane said.

"I'm Nurse Monico; You don't remember me?" the woman said.

"Why would I know you?"

The nurse looked around Diane, eyebrows raised.

"Won't you excuse me," Diane said. A large hand came

down on her shoulder.

"Ma'am?" Diane turned and looked. The security guard stood more than a foot taller than both women and was as wide as both women side by side.. His eyes looked at Diane with a bit of pity. He wore a black face mask.

"Yes?" Diane stepped back from the guard. "Do not touch me. I haven't done anything wrong."

"Mrs. Osman does not have an appointment here," the woman in scrubs said.

"How do you know what appointments I have and don't have; you're not my attending physician!" Diane crossed her arms and seethed in the woman's direction.

"There was a glitch in our system," the security guard gave a small shrug toward the nurse. "But she popped up with a flag after her sanitization." He then turned to Diane. "Do you have a spouse or someone you can call?"

"Her husband passed a week before she had her miscarriage; it was the virus," the nurse said to the security guard, then she sighed and shook her head. Her eyes looked on with pity while Diane leaned away from the man, trying to break free, and giving weak screeches of, "let me go."

"I'll take care of it, nurse." He looked at Diane. "Mrs. Osman, you need to come with me."

"I'll do no such thing," Diane said. "This is unnecessary harassment. Call Dr. Case this instant! I demand it."

Just then two more security guards came, one from behind the giant of a guard and one from behind the nurse.

"Please don't make this difficult," the first guard said. "We're not going to hurt you, but you need to leave here."

"I do not need to leave; I need to see the doctor." Diane's voice grew very shrill. People were starting to stare. She ripped off her own mask. "You just hate me because I'm immune!"

"Please, Mrs. Osman," the security guard lowered his voice.

Sirens began to wail outside. Diane looked around her. She knew she wasn't safe, but she didn't understand why they were pestering her with this nonsense.

"Mrs. Osman," the nurse spoke up. "You can't keep coming back here; you lost your baby."

Diane looked down and saw her dress, it was full of blood. She screamed, "Why am I bleeding?"

"Mrs. Osman, you're not bleeding," the nurse said.

Diane tried to speak, but instead everything went dark.

The ambulance arrived, and the processing of visitors to the medical center continued. The medics loaded Mrs. Osman into the ambulance and took her back to Saint Birgitta's Women's Hospital just a few blocks down Cherry Hill. As they wheeled her into the emergency room, Diane awoke and heard the train along the waterfront call out a mourning cry. And she began to cry with it.

Artist's Bio: Gayll Morrison is an artist living in Snoqualmie, Washington. She was born in Calgary Alberta and attended the Alberta College of Art before getting completely side-tracked with a 20 year career in software engineering. Now retired she has the time to get back to her long-neglected pursuit of oil painting. As an oil painter Gayll explores aspects of light, space, and water in what are often landscapes, sometimes abstract, and occasionally both. Gayll is a founding member of the Art Gallery of SnoValley and a member of the Mt. Si Artist Guild.

Author's Bio: Casondra Brewster has been in love with writing and books for a half century. She's a veteran, wife, mother, teacher, activist, microfarmer, motorcyclist, sailor, traveler and dog rescuer. Currently residing in the Cascade Foothills, she is the founder and moderator of SnoValley Writes! a small but mighty writing group that works to help its members reach new literary peaks and expand literary horizons in its community.

Photo: Tara Sreekumar, plentyopixels.com

THE OLD TRACKS

⊗

Madison Wachter

Madison Wachter Tommia Wright

Madison's Inspiration: The piece was inspired by the drive I have taken many times from the lowlands to the mountains. I have driven this with love in my heart, pain in my heart, excitement and wonder, following the former path of the train that was built over 100 years ago along the I-90 corridor. I incorporated the mists flowing through the valleys that have captivated my imagination for my entire life, picturing the train following the tracks of old over bridges, becoming lost to history, lost to time, disappearing into the mists forever.

Madsion's Partnership: I chose to work loosely with my paired author. I asked her for a brief description of what she was hoping for and I decided to paint a moon phase depiction over mountains strung together by mists. This was based on her description of what her hopes were. My artist style is very personal and I have a hard time diverting from what my heart wants to paint so our approach of a loose collaboration worked very well. I was able to make art that worked well with her story while staying true to my style.

Tommia's Partnership: My artist showed me one of her pieces and wanted to make something new. I loved what she showed me and asked for something similar, with planets and more stars in the sky. She delivered!

Tommia's Inspiration: Story inspiration – what if someone wanted to escape the nonsense all around them? What if another being, wanting to save all in harm's way, heard the wish?

The Liberation of Stranded Travelers is the start of an unexpected journey that would be out of this world.

THE L.O.S.T. TRAIN: AN UNEXPECTED JOURNEY
FANTASY
by Tommia Wright

History is a race between education and catastrophe.
– H.G. Wells

Roberta pushed her way into the first unlocked door available, dodging the cloudburst above, the hail of rubber bullets, and the scattering of debris. She knelt below the boarded windows and took her dog's face in her hands. "Shush, Vera! No-bark! When we get into space, you can bark all you want."

"Ah, in space, you think no one will hear Vera bark?"

Roberta looked up at the apron-draped gentleman, dark curly hair atop, going in various directions. His dark mustache and graying beard did nothing to hide the welcoming smile on his face as he held a towel out for her. If she were to guess, he was her age, maybe a few years older. The accent, however, was a challenge to place.

She rose slowly, gave a nod of thanks and took the towel.

He motioned for her to join him at a small table in the back, Vera close on her heels. Before she could ask about the unsecured door, he said, "Looters don't go for coffee the same way they do computers and cell phones." He slid a plate of sliced warm sourdough bread and a glass of water her way.

Roberta removed her bag from her arm and took in the décor. She'd seen the window display from the sidewalk before, but hadn't suspected such a cozy, yet gallery feel to the place. Books, puzzles, and games filled the many short shelves, and small booths lined the wall. Perhaps half a dozen other people were present that she'd failed to notice at first. She gazed at the hand-painted wooden sign behind the counter that read, *Coffee with Colleagues.*

"That's me, Mr. Colleagues. Call me Andy."

Roberta would have sworn this was one of the many businesses forced to close, thanks to the government ordered shutdown months ago. "How long have you been here?" she asked.

"Long enough," he said. "Long enough. What do you say to a good Frigg'a-atrecme? Oh, wait, I mean a Friday afternoon tea, yes?" He poured a steaming cup and pushed it toward her on the nearby counter. "Always my favorite thing to look forward to. Fridays, a funny way to call the end of the week."

"Oh? And what do you call the end of employment? I used to have a job aiding the destitute, but you're looking at someone on the other side of the desk. I've joined the many millions that I used to help." She cautiously sipped at the tea.

He smiled. "I see you as one of the billions and billions of souls still vibrant with life."

The booming outside grew louder, closer. "Thunder's getting worse," she said.

"It isn't thunder." He ran to the doors and helped a couple of people inside. Roberta recognized her neighbor, a photojournalist for the local news. She rushed over to help seat them in one of the booths along the wall. Vera sat still, close to the neighbor.

"There's more coming," another person said, handing off their walking stick to Andy who rushed to help. For a fleeting moment, Roberta thought she recognized the shorter woman with the long hair, glasses used as a hairband.

Andy vanished into the darkness beyond the door. Roberta lost track of how long he was out there. She focused her energy on her neighbor, and tried to ignore the sound of helicopters and hailing bullets on the other side of the door. When someone had joked about Hell on Earth, she never imagined this.

Dozens of people poured into the café, Andy the last to enter. He locked the door behind him and strode towards the back, laying the walking stick on the counter.

Roberta ran over and comforted a few of the incoming that were injured. A medic who was part of the crowd relieved her, and she went after Andy. "What's going on? Who are you?"

He gave a quick nod to someone behind her. "I told you. Andy Colleagues."

Roberta fell onto a stool as calming music played overhead.

Her muscles relaxed and her heart rate slowed. Vera trotted over and lay down by her feet. She wondered if she'd been drugged. "Fine. Don't tell me." She stroked Vera's ears absently.

When Andy strolled by, Roberta frowned and tried again. "What's going on and who exactly are you?"

"I told you. Andy Colleagues. Consider me your guide, storyteller, translator, mate, and for the moment," he smiled as his hands rushed over a series of levers and buttons behind the counter, "mini-conductor." Looking behind her, she saw all the new arrivals sitting in booths that weren't there before, and the door to the street had vanished.

Andy came around the counter and handed her a fresh cup of tea. Welcome to the L.O.S.T. Train. Well, the Galaxy Lounge until your sleeper is ready."

Roberta wondered if she should have something stronger to drink. "I think one of us has lost their mind."

Andy's shoulders fell. "Oh dear. Rather fumbling through this again, aren't I? The L.O.S.T. Train is for Liberation of Stranded Travelers. That would be you and many of your lot here. And before I forget, in case anything should happen, here is your Whistler's Walker and Lean-Tow."

She set the tea on a little table at her side and ran her thumb over the polished antler whistle secured at the top of the stick. It reminded her of the hiking props she and her friends had purchased on vacation at The Olympic Peninsula. "You fought off the bullies outside with a walking stick?" she asked him in disbelief.

Andy shook his head. "It's not a stick, it's a Whistler's Walker. I used the Enveloper, here." He pointed. An atmospheric protector should you choose to step off-world along the way and want to keep living. I deployed it to escape the tear gas."

"Right," Roberta said, afraid to accept the possibility. Along the way where? She set the Lean-Tow on the table next to her. It looked like a rock-climbing rope – too short to even be a belt.

She recovered her tea and watched the others in silence. One figure held a hint of familiarity to her. The cacophony of different languages reminded her of a trip on the Staten Island Ferry when she was a child. It seemed a long time ago. "Who are these people?" she mumbled.

"Oh, everyone who boarded here is from Earth," he told her, and he pulled up a stool by her side. "Wait until you hear the cosmic collection of communications and the symphony it creates – spectacular!"

Roberta shivered in her seat and clung to the odd walking stick.

Andy re-filled the teacup at her elbow. "Oh dear. No need for discomfort. Your items, along with your pet, Vera, are in your room – or about to be, or could be...well, should be."

He paused, so she nodded once. Vera and her bag snapped away and air swirled against her leg where her dog previously rested. "So are the whole human race and the wildlife being rescued? Like Noah's Ark or something?"

Andy seemed to age at the mention of the question. "More than that. Stations like the one you entered through are locations facing planetary crises. The refugees, like you lot, are boarded because of their souls, their stance or beliefs, and importantly, their spirits.

Roberta noticed the person the medic had helped was laughing and drinking tea. "Everyone that was injured appears fine now."

"D'Bethany's a great healer," Andy told her. "Oh, and see that svelte figure in the blue beside D'Bethany? That's Giovedi. It failed to pay attention to the last meteor shower and was therefore stranded on a moon in the Tadpole Galaxy. Tends to be a bit of a snob against mono-planetary travelers."

Giovedi changed posture and started shouting. Roberta only heard a few words before the stick was yanked from her hands.

Andy smiled apologetically. "Almost forgot. This here is a Babbel-Fish Vertebra. Place your digit over the mouthpiece of the whistle and you'll be understood by those you are speaking to. Place your digit over the air hole on top of the whistle and it will translate whatever is said around you so you can understand. Usually."

Roberta wrapped her index finger over the air hole on top of the whistle. "I think I got the gist of what was said," Roberta told him as they watched D'Bethany (who looked more like Dr. Amy Fields to her) led Giovedi away.

Andy shook his head. "Let me find the best words for what was about to follow." He tilted his head before he began. "Corrupt celery coward, wait, cowardly cellar commanders will get their wish and die out like disintegrating ashes."

"How does that fit with your soul/spirit selection process?" Roberta challenged.

"How could your earth endure so many factions and faulty leaders, let alone individuals, who believe they have a right to decide who is...disposable. Why don't more of you speak up about how disgusting that is?" he countered.

Roberta put her hand firmly over her teacup as Andy

reached to pour. She helped herself to a bottle of water, and he poured a cup of tea for himself. "So Earth's screwed up. We know that. I expected alien lifeforms would be smart enough not to stop by."

"Foolish, deadly decisions aren't limited to Earth. They're made on Mars, the Triangulum Galaxy, the Sombrero Galaxy. There are even travelers, refugees from the Pinwheel – and I already mentioned the Tadpole Galaxy."

"And where are you from, Andy? I don't see a third eye or a wrinkled forehead. So, let me guess, two hearts?"

He sipped his tea and gave her a wistful smile. "I'm from the Clement Clouds of Neptune. I boarded the train when the Caturrah Catastrophe struck. Like your planet, we had time to prepare, to act with urgency. We could have avoided disaster. Fellow artisans told the tales, singers sung the songs and yet we were ignored...for eons. Not many of us remain."

"As for my anatomy...two hearts? That's sad. Not to discriminate, but I've four, thank you. One for living, one for loving, one that's broken and another that's mending – latter two always in rotation. Then, I've three lungs, three ears, two eyes, as you can see, and my extremities are the same as yours, even if I am better on digits than you." He gave her the same smile she had been greeted with.

"Anything we could have done differently?" Roberta asked.

Andy shook his head. "The mistakes are the same for the failed: dismiss, deny, distort, deflect, deal death, destroy. Those who remain here are going to get what they want – the old, the weak, the 'other', the 'deemed useless' to be gone. If they had only looked in a mirror when they spoke from their dark souls.

"On the bright side, at least you'll have some great

company on the way to Secunda Opportunitas. You'll love Russo, a fun historian from Amabo. Lost everything during 'The Great Race', sadly. Fascinating stories, that's for certain. And we'll have plenty of time to explore and relax, too."

Roberta felt the slight lurch of the train as it left the station. "Define 'time.'"

"It's a relative concept, best measured on a routine of your liking. I stopped labeling a while ago. Only enlightening events remain as my markers. Other more practical gatherings happen too, but I receive a reminder, so I don't bother remembering."

She took it all in, mind racing with more questions than answers. "Does this mean if I need you to guide me, it'll be via reminders?"

"Oh no. My suite's next to yours. Unless there's somewhere else you'd rather be?"

Roberta sighed and scanned the room behind her. All the others had gone. "How is it that you know me so well?"

"I know *about* you – how you think your job is your identity, how you put others first and carry the weight of the world on your shoulders – like D'Bethany did, however she did it literally. But I don't *know* you. For example, how did you live on that planet for half a century and never give yourself time and permission to explore?"

He came around the counter and held an elbow her way. When she accepted, he visibly brightened in mood and spirit. "Come on, I'll take you to the Wishing View Window Room! We can still see the Canadian Rockies, the Aurora Borealis, and any other wonder on this planet as we leave."

"You've done this often?" she asked.

Andy shrugged. "As a guide? You're my first proper charge. As the sole conductor departing a station, my first time there, too. Oh, hold on to your Whistler's Walker, and don't forget your Lean-Tow."

"Yes, what is a Lean-Tow?" When she held it up, its length matched her forearm.

"It's in dormant form now. But should you wish to step out into the slipstream, it'll lengthen to whatever size you need. I'll show you the controls before you use it. Well, after we've practiced in the anti-grav room, of course."

Andy led Roberta to the back wall of the Galaxy Lounge. All of the booths were gone, and a narrow strip of blurry space ran along the seam between floor and wall. Within the blur, lines of smeared light zipped by horizontally. "The slipstream," Andy explained. "Mind the gap."

He pulled her forward and they stepped across the slipstream into a car made of glass that hadn't been there moments before. D'Bethany sat on a smooth wooden bench near the center of the car gazing at the desert scene that stretched out before them. The gentleman next to her focused on something in the distance. Roberta studied D'Bethany's profile, then shook her head to dismiss a strange thought.

Andy led Roberta through the crowd to a bench on the opposite side of the car, steering her focus towards the window. "We'll join her for mealtime later. Blink now, however, and you'll miss all that you want to see while you can."

"So, Earth's going to blow up, is that what you're telling me?" Her mind replayed all the cinematic versions of humanity's demise, ending with the manic cry of a lone astronaut after finding the remains of a once meaningful and symbolic statue buried in sand.

Andy's laughter broke her from her musing. "Goodness, no! Be in the now, Roberta. You've allowed yourself to be torn in opposite directions for too long. What do you want to enjoy at this moment?"

She sighed. She couldn't take in the view with so many questions whirling in her mind. "First things, first. What – ?"

Andy finished her question. "– language are they speaking? Ongota."

Roberta shook her head as she recalled a magazine article about endangered languages. "There's only one speaker of that language left; he's the last."

"On your planet," Andy said, spinning his Whistler's Walker between his hands.

"Back in the lounge, I heard another variant of a Native American Language, from an elder. Only two members remain from that tribe."

"On your planet," Andy repeated. "You'll have to learn what you unlearned, Roberta. Great news is, you're in good company. You're a child, like me."

Roberta laughed. "The expression is, 'unlearn what you have learned.' If I'm a child, what is a five-year-old?"

"Learn what you've unlearned," he repeated. He opened his hand and showed her a glimmering, multi-colored stone. "The youngsters, no matter what realm, are the bright future for us all. Gems – galactical, eternal marvelous souls. Plenty of time to learn and play and realize that a new start can be refreshing."

Roberta took in the view of the Borealis Lights, then other majestic wonders she had on her bucket list. It broke her heart to think that this would be the last time she'd see such wonders.

"Maybe the journey isn't about becoming anything. Maybe it's about unbecoming everything that isn't really you," Andy told her. "Your world, like many throughout the galaxy, will recover its original beauty over time.

"In the meanwhile, you can stay on the train, wrapped in things that bring comfort, connecting with many who are different, yet similar. You can settle on your final destination...The galaxies are ready for discovery."

Roberta noticed D'Bethany and the svelte Giovani were gone. Instead of a desert, a magnificent view of the Great Barrier Reef filled the direction they had faced. Turning to look at Andy, she saw loneliness and love, of empathy and exploration. "Well, you said you were my guide, so where to next?"

Andy smiled. "Go settle into your suite first and reunite with Vera. Time might be relative, but energy's another story. Rest will do you good. Then, it shall be a proper feast."

She followed him through the doors of the glass car, surprised to step into the sleeper car so soon.

"Where you wish to be is where you will be," Andy told her. "The Wishing View Window Room will always be in the slipstream."

He gestured for her to hold her hand out in front of a panel. "Only you and those you choose can enter your space," he said. He leaned against the door frame, leaning the Whistler's Walker just inside the room as she entered.

"It's larger than I expected a train car room to be," Roberta said. She was relieved to see Vera was apparently so relaxed she didn't even get up to greet them. And as Andy had said, her belongings were here – and far more than the bag she'd had on her arm. There was an assortment from everything she owned – all the things she wanted to use first. "I worried it would be cramped and I wouldn't have what I needed."

"No. Again, where you wish to be is where you will be, even here." He gestured towards her left. "I'm next door. Knock on the wall when you're ready for dinner."

The wonderful space reminded her of her childhood home – her first home – and her dream home all at once. Even the view was the one she had always wanted, a sandy shore. She tousled Vera's fur by her cheeks. Too restless to sleep, Roberta stepped back out to get Andy.

They sat in one of the larger booths in the dining car with D'Bethany and Russo.

"That is why I liked your earlier leader in your country, that 'can do' attitude," Russo said. "On Amabo, there was too much hesitation, with leaders more concerned with how our culture would look through history's eyes, than what to do in the moment. They spent so much time erasing all traces of what they considered faults that I am not sure if anyone truly remembers who we are or were. That is why this time in history interests me so much."

Roberta shook her head. "Wait, so we are, from your point of view, in your past?"

"In a manner of speaking, yes, and no. My sense of time is...fluid. What you call the past, the future, I experience as... just being."

"Be mindful of your health," D'Bethany reminded the

historian.

"I am. If you'll excuse me, I have some new arrivals to meet."

Roberta stared at D'Bethany and struggled to put some pieces together. "I don't mean to be rude, but I feel like I've seen you before."

Andy took his time with his salad as D'Bethany smiled. "Who do I remind you of?"

"You obviously, but, I thought your name was Dr. Amy Fields. And then there's Dr. Cross, Secretary Daniels, General Charles, not that it makes any sense. How could one person be the entire task force, right?"

"It can be tiring," D'Bethany said. "I am myself and those you've named. It is – the nature of my kind to be one and many, as needed. I only wish I had done better."

Roberta shook her head slowly. "Secretary Daniels lied about the progress. He lied."

"Yes, I did," D'Bethany said. "I did it so the Vaccine Teams could live. The president didn't know my true being and I used it to my advantage. Other teams did it successfully, and saved many lives in the countries they were assigned to."

Andy spoke up. "To be fair, some of the teams did secure leadership roles and reinforced necessary measures by gaining enough support. You bought people time – gave them hope."

D'Bethany smiled again. "Fair enough. If only hope and good would spread as quickly as the deadly viruses do." She stood. "I'm going to get some rest after I check in on my charges. Speaking of time, there's a certain story that should be shared right about now, yes?" She walked away.

Roberta sighed. "I didn't mean to offend her."

"You didn't." Andy leaned forward and his brow crumpled as if in pain. His hand flew to his chest. Roberta rose to yell for the doctor, but he pulled her down. "I'm fine," he said.

"No you're not. You're hurting."

He shook his head. "I just need to get back to my room. Would you – ?"

In a matter of steps, they were back in the corridor outside their quarters. Roberta lifted Andy's hand towards the panel. He shook his head again. "You're granted permission," he said. Roberta set her own hand on the panel and marveled as it opened at her touch.

As they entered Andy's room, a tea setting appeared on the small table between two recliners. He motioned for her to take a chair as he started to pour the tea. "We never got to finish our Frigg'a-atrecme," he told her.

She cautiously took a sip and was surprised to taste the familiar, calming blend of rooibos, orange peel, lemon verbena, rose, and lavender. Smiling, she said, "This is what I splurged on with my last paycheck. Stop distracting me. What happened to you at dinner?"

He took a long deep breath, held it a while, then let it out slowly before he answered. "Heart rotation, nothing more. Remember, one breaks, one mends, etcetera, etcetera."

She nodded. "Does it happen often?"

"It happens when it happens. My body still struggles to adjust to it, but it will get used to it, in time."

Roberta's face folded in worry.

"Oh, no, no, no," he pleaded. "I saw enough of that

expression from the others and my family. Before it happened, I loved with all of my hearts. Evidently, there was a problem with that. "When the Caturrah Catastrophes happened, almost destroying us, we were challenged to change. Many found comfort in the new ways that went against what we had always believed; a small number clung to the old ways, dogmatically." He paused. "Because of how an artist's hearts beat, the conflicts were devastating for some of us – including me One of my hearts broke. I didn't realize I was dying inside, I just felt tired – yet I still loved those around me unconditionally.

"All the others chose to use their Lean-Tows to enter the slipstream and settle on a new home planet of their choosing rather than wait on the L.O.S.T. train to arrive at the new destination."

Roberta leaned forward and took his hand. "Why did you stay?"

"D'Bethany." He smiled at Roberta reassuringly. "She accepted me as her charge – showed me that what my family considered a defect was a gift that needed to grow. Live, create, mend – that's the normal heart rotation of my kind. D'Bethany helped me reset and adjust, but still allowed me to keep my broken heart."

"I don't understand why you think a broken heart is a good thing to have?" Roberta said.

"I feel too much, sometimes. It happens – listening to others' stories, songs... I can't help but feel with them. Sometimes, it's too much to bear – the sadness, the pain, for example. They weigh heavy on the heart and it breaks. There are enjoyable moments, too. For example, it's fun arguing with Giovedi, challenging its limited views of the universe. I often find limited views of my own. It taught me the fluidity of time and how one can create the most magnificent of celebrations by weaving a multitude of notes and creating with the plentiful planetary palettes from everywhere always."

Roberta smiled. "You're too much, Andy."

Andy smiled. "I experience extreme wonders like Giovedi's joy and extreme sorrow when I meet those who come on board with suffering and pain. I'm still trying to figure out how you humans do all of that with only one heart?"

Roberta looked down at her chest and back to Andy's shining eyes.

"Here people heal from their pain. You'll see, every being on the L.O.S.T. train has the same...dream, ideal, hope, priority. Love flourishing and life thriving without strife, starvation, or war. Every passenger has their own story to share, but they reach to find similarities among their differences."

"Like the languages," Roberta said.

"Like the languages," Andy repeated.

She poured them both another cup, surprised the clear pot was still full. "How do you handle conflicts, disagreements, power and chaos?"

"Listening. Breathing. It takes time to realize that murder and violence isn't a means, but rather a brutal end. On Secunda Opportunitas all lifeforms get a fresh start. Eventually they'll choose whether or not to return to their original worlds when restored after the effects of the viruses are gone."

The optimistic pessimist in her had to doubt. "Won't the fresh start for those from Earth just end up in the same condition? The human heart is crafty enough to rot from within. No laws have cured that. No arts or wars or schooling... Nothing is death-proof."

Andy sighed. "It is. It's a matter of encouragement. All of our stories are intertwined, connected like the constellations. It only requires our spirits to race fast enough to contribute spectacular stories, and share them with all of our worlds. From these ashes within us, embers of an illuminated infinity can emerge."

Roberta looked out the large window behind him, surprised by the colorful view. "Is that what your home looked like?" she asked.

Andy nodded and his eyelids drooped. "A part of it, yes. The view is what you wish. Imagination's a wondrous thing. We should pay Russo a visit – the polarscapes would remind you of Alaska from your planet, as they remind me of E'ghiaccio from mine."

"We can go see them another time. Someone could use a proper rest." Roberta grabbed the blanket from the back of her chair and covered Andy with it. His chair reclined in response.

She tip-toed away, but turned back near the doorway and watched as the room transformed – lights dimming, save for a mobile of stars dancing near his head. She smiled.

When she stepped into the hallway, she jumped. Dr. Fields stood there. "He's resting," she told the medic.

"Just as you should be."

Roberta invited the other woman in. The space had transformed into the familiar living room she enjoyed. "What should I call you?" she asked.

"Whatever feels most comfortable to you, Roberta. I've no preference."

"When you exist in so many places at once, how do you fight fatigue, Amy?"

"It's a matter of allocating energy as needed. For instance, I knew Andy was in excellent hands with you, given your caring spirit, so I rested. I might remind you to pace yourself too." Amy smiled. "You've been through a lot recently, as have I. During the news conferences, it took all I had not to strike the commander as he lied, but I made it through. When it came to research, I drew on the persistence, the positivity from the others, and hoped we were close to a cure for the virus and we could stay to fight it. But when my relations told me of the strains they saw and felt across the planet, I knew – we all knew – it was time to get you all to safety."

"You saved Andy from Neptune, Russo from Amabo. How long have you been doing this?"

"Not as long as the Conductor, I can tell you that. Long enough to know that we can rest once every lifeform has settled on Secugunda Opportunitas. There are many cars on this train and I'd like to help assure everyone remains healthy. How are you doing, Roberta?"

She shrugged. "It's a lot to take in to be honest. Last day of work, let alone last day on my planet – who knew? First day of meeting...four different entities I never knew existed before? I think I'm doing all right so far."

Amy smiled. "Good to hear. Good to hear. You know where the View Room is if your window doesn't allow for a large enough visual. Tomorrow after breakfast, we can explore more of the train – check out the libraries, the singing towers, the Proteus Shores..." She paused. "What is it?"

"Was it safe to leave Andy alone? Is he really going to be alright?"

Amy nodded. "He is. Now that you're here, he is. Someone who can help him keep his hearts' rotation from spinning swiftly between past and future is a definite present. I'll see you in the morning."

Roberta smiled. "Thank you. I'll see you in the morning, too."

After Amy left, Roberta sought the refuge of her bedroom and reflected on a remarkable day. Time was relative, she remembered. Now mattered more than past or future. Yet, it felt as if she had known Andy Colleagues her entire life, just as she was starting to know herself.

Artist's Bio: Madison Wachter is the creator behind the AshenNewt brand. She has always believed in the creative mind, and the power of imagination. Ever since she was young, she's been enamored with stories, telling them and desperately trying to express them. Through art she found ways to tell visual stories of places she's seen and places she loves. Art taught her about patience, belief, self-trust and diligence, but the most important lesson she learned is discipline. Art taught her to slow down, not only with creative pursuits, but with everything. To see what's around her and appreciate the journey. It taught her there's a delicate balance between pushing herself and working hard. It taught her there's nothing more important than giving love to every moment of the creative process and life, no matter how hard it is.

Author's Bio: Tommia Wright is a lifelong learner, writer, creator, believer, and dreamer.
Born in Seattle and raised in the Valley, chances are the photographer – and self-professed bibliophile – will be found brazenly browsing indie-bookstores, in search of new writers, despite the self-imposed book-buying ban. The local logophile knew writing was the right path for her because she was 'born

to it.' (Besides, not being related to the famous Wright Brothers, the dreams of becoming a pilot lasted as long as the initial flight at Kitty Hawk.)

Photo: Tara Sreekumar, plentyopixels.com

BIRDHOUSE WITH TRAIN ⊗ Pepper Allphin

Pepper Allphin   Victoria Bastedo

Pepper's Inspiration: I chose the birdhouse in part because I have been creating and selling a lot of birdhouses. It's a remarkably great way to recycle old jewelry, mementos, greeting cards, toys....you name it!! And the littlest of details gives me so much delight! Lol! I am not a writer but I am an avid reader and I can invent wild stories in seconds when I look at something that catches my eye. So all the little details present unlimited options to me.

Pepper's Partnership: Pepper's work was complete before meeting Victoria, but after reading part of the story Pepper told Victoria: Wow I love this story so so much! Just my style...I would read it on my own.

Victoria's Partnership: Pepper and I talked about each other's art, and how we were pleased to spark off of it. Victoria told Pepper: These are magical! I really like the train flying up through the countryside and the lighthouse behind it. I could imagine that taking place in the story.

Victoria's Inspiration: It was my grandson, of course! He loved his Thomas train as an 18-month-old. It got lost several times and it was always tragic for him at bedtime. I thought like all infant stages it would pass, but it lingered for years. He saw something in that Thomas train, that captivated and took him places.

FOLIO THE BRAVE
CHILDREN'S STORY
by Victoria Bastedo

Toy trains are color blind. No, that's not quite true, what they are is color-bright, for they can only see primary colors, with a few bold additions like pumpkin orange and grape purple. I was told this simple truth by Anatole, who is three years old and also, a genius.

We were lying, stomachs down and a little damp, on the grass of the backyard. The little train was a few inches in front of us. 'Folio', was the name he had been given. He was light blue, and his painted sides were faded of their original detail. Most of his face was still there, for despite his smile, it was a stubborn face. His huge round nose was a magnet, and his bunny-tail backside had a magnet of equal size and heaviness.

I thought that's what made Folio special, a stand-out from all other fist-sized toy trains. That cold and weighty metal dot on either end, it didn't shout it was better than plastic, but it hinted. Folio was top-rate, which was why his left cheek-spot had been rubbed off.

Folio doesn't like grass, Anatole informed me. Nor the inside of bathtubs.

"Mud?"

"Oh, yes, mud is fine. Trains prefer bathing in mud."

A moment of silence fell on us and we studied Folio, who couldn't lie down straight on his train wheels because the grass tickled his belly.

"Will you take Folio with you on your trip to see your grandpa?" I asked.

Anatole didn't give me a direct answer, but he did say planes are really color blind, because they can only see white, gray and pale-blue sky. This was when he told me Folio was Anatole's best train-friend, who nobody else could see.

"Ah," I said. "An Imaginary Friend. A rare but quality breed."

"Folio says imaginary people have more fun than others. He comes from an imaginary world."

"What does this world look like?"

"Obviously, the trees are primary green, and the sky is primary blue. Folio knows green isn't a primary color but it's brave."

I pointed out that Folio must like going on adventures, being that he's a train and lives in an imaginary world. Anatole agreed. Folio did like those things.

"Then perhaps Folio will like going with you when you fly

to see your grandpa."

Anatole sat up, snatched Folio into his little-boy fist, and threw him hard. The train landed a few feet away. Although on his side, I could still spy Folio's open eye. He was a stubborn locomotive, alright.

"Folio can't come. Imaginary worlds don't exist when a boy grows big."

"Imaginary worlds do exist, for how else could Folio chug-chug or toot?"

Anatole didn't feel like arguing. Instead, he cried like a three-year-old until his mother came out and spoke to him. He didn't feel reasonable either. Boys his age get tired, she said. Even geniuses. Anatole went inside, for his hand was tugged that way.

I stood in the backyard, listening. Anatole's bedroom window was on the main floor. His window was open in a two-inch crack. It was locked that way, so no burglar could get inside.

He did his business in the bathroom, had a drink of water, and climbed into his bed. But he continued to yell. Three-year-old's must yell a lot about the injustices of the world and other outrages.

After a moment the mother came outside. She bent and picked up Folio, and pushed him through the crack of the window. He fell with a loud thud onto the bedroom floor inside. A few seconds later Anatole stopped yelling. He and Folio took a nap.

It's the perfect time to make my report. I pressed the button on my wrist and shrunk down until the spiky grass surrounded me like jungle trees. The closest entrance was half-buried in a mole hill, or perhaps this mound of dirt had been dug by Anatole himself. A plastic man lay forgotten, a toy of long ago, who, by virtue of the dirt hill covering his chest and one whole arm, had avoided the blades of the lawn mower. His legs were scissored open and his turned head hid his face. The toy didn't speak to me. Forgotten toys froze when no one played with them. Especially the plastic ones. They disappeared into the Land of Happy Remembering – remnants of the world they'd inhabited when a child's imagination brought them to life.

I was able to make this toy my door. Frozen toys always left the doorway into Playland wide open.

I breathed a sigh of relief when I'd left the real world behind. Around me comforting colors coated the landscape. Primary yellow sun, a smiling circle in the sky, smooth blue of pond, curled in the shape of a kidney bean, and the bright red headquarters, a two-story building with painted black lines – all seemed to wave at me as I crossed the pure-green lawn.

I entered the building and adjusted my natty uniform. I cocked my hat at just the right jaunty angle. I walked up to the supervisor's door and rapped a sharp knock.

"Entrance!" called a vigorous voice from inside.

I marched into Colonel Waistcoat's office. On the wall, calendars with dancing numbers kicked in their rows. Out the window, the trainyard housed several happy trains tooting and chugging. Colonel Waistcoat stood broad and cheerful. His face was brown plastic, and his hair was black. His blue coat boasted double rows of buttons, and the regalia on his shoulders was bright yellow.

"Report, Captain Spyglass!" he commanded.

"Yes, sir, Colonel! I was able to visit Anatole. Folio let me take his place as Imaginary Friend for the interview."

"And what did you discover, Captain?"

"It's true, Sir! Anatole intends to leave Folio behind. The book may close in peril!"

"Hold your hat, Captain!"

"Yes, Sir!"

"Has Lieutenant Folio devised a plan to stay with the boy?"

"He says it will be dangerous, Colonel, but he will fall into action at sunrise!"

"How brave is Lieutenant Folio!" the Colonel sang, and his cheeks shook while his barrel-chest filled. Outside in Playland, a bright red-and-blue-dressed band of flute-whistlers, drummers and bugle players came marching by.

"Yes, he is, Sir!" I cried. "Hurrah!"

Later that day, when I was about to leave Playland to enter the real world, I discovered Lieutenant Folio was tumbling.

"Tumbling?" I asked him. "What for?" I could see him, rolling and bouncing off hills, with his button nose down and his black wheels up.

"Because I'm in Rough-n-Tumble, Captain Spyglass!" he answered.

Of course. Perhaps, in the real-world Folio was stuck in the dryer. But things could be worse.

I pushed the button on my wrist and grew to my Imaginary Friend size. I adjusted my cap to a not-so-jaunty angle, so that it was level across my forehead, and reported to Anatole to learn what had transpired.

Aha. Anatole grasped a cardboard poster tube, with each of the two ends taped down. I could hear the clunk of something inside as he waved it around.

"May I ask what you're doing?"

"I'm going to mail Folio away!" he told me.

"Where are you mailing him?"

"To the Land of Little Kids Who Can't Afford a Toy."

I'd heard about places like that. I didn't tell Anatole, but it was just possible Folio would never reach this fabulous land at all. And even if he did, he might get handed to the wrong kid. A kid who didn't like trains, or didn't like them with button noses, or with one cheek-mark rubbed off. Stubborn trains, even those used to Rough-n-Tumble, weren't always tough enough to make it in such places.

"You're a little kid, aren't you? Why not keep Folio by your side?"

"Because I'm going to school. That means I can't be little anymore. My grandpa said I'm a big boy now!"

Oh, no. Not that! The term, 'big boy' was frowned upon in Playland.

I wondered how much information I was authorized to divulge. "Details of a secret mission have just come from headquarters," I said. "Lieutenant Folio has been ordered to remain in contact!"

"Whose orders?" asked Anatole.

"From high up. Colonel Waistcoat, himself!"

Anatole's hand dropped. The poster tube shot downward, and the toy train rocketed out past the tape and landed face forward on the cement patio. Folio rolled a few feet, and his metal button nose shone in the sun. His cheerful eye and chirpy smile made him irresistible, I thought.

Tense seconds passed. Then the door to the house opened, and Anatole's mother came out. The afternoon was over, and it was time to have dinner. A bath would follow, and some books and then bed. To my relief Anatole did not leave us outside to face the big night by ourselves, nor the cloying dew of morning.

Hours later Folio and I were on the move. It was deep in the night, and we traveled through Mount Blanket towards Sheet-Tuck Ford. Folio was determined to go through with his mission, though I stood steadfast against his plan. I cautioned and warned and begged him to reconsider.

It would be better, I thought, to become a plastic, forgotten toy in the Land of Happy Remembering – with his eyes open – than to be lost in the unpredictable world of Dreamland.

"That's a major exit!" I told him. Imaginary Friends often left town through Dreamland. The book would be closed for them, forever.

"I can make it back!" Folio insisted. "It's the only way!"

"But Anatole will also miss you if you're lost in Dreamland. Isn't it the same as him leaving you behind?"

"No! Anatole can't leave me behind!" We were just rounding the soft, snowy slopes of Pillow Peak, and Folio paused our journey. "It's important, Spyglass! Becoming a 'big boy' before you're meant to is a heavy burden. I must explain this to Anatole!"

We'd reached it – the cuddly entryway through the Caves of Comforter. A dreamer always leaves a Wink-Window open into Dreamland if you burrow far enough under the pillow of a sleeping child.

"Farewell, Brave Lieutenant!" I told Folio.

"Keep watch, Captain!"

"Be assured I will." I said, and I snuck my spyglass into Folio's cargo compartment as he departed.

I straightened my crooked cap, level across my eyebrows. It wasn't easy to stand straight and tall on Downy Mattress, but I didn't falter. When Folio's knock opened the Wink-Window into Dreamland, I was able to watch where he went with my spyglass.

Oh, Dreamland was all that I'd heard about. A fearsome place indeed. Little children, even if they were geniuses like Anatole, hardly understood the world they visited each day – the real world. I can't say I understand it myself. Dreamland was connected to the store-closet of imagination, and that's why toys avoid it. Alas, for brave Folio.

Playland lives in the front room of a child's imagination. Bright Happenings overcome Big Troubles in Playland. There are marching bands on standby, and realms of green, rolling hills, cheerful curving train tracks, dots of daisy flowers and blue skies with clouds like white puffy sheep.

Dreamland has many dark curtains, draped from the endless ceiling of Wonder-Why. There are almost no bright colors at all.

Folio chugged bravely forward. Though surrounded by the perils of Dreamland, he was able to play his tune.

Toot, toot on the tootle downs, Bright button and snookie darns,

Boats and bubbles and cookie cheeks,

Books about moons with purple streaks!

Toot, toot, I say toodle-oo!

There's more time for me and you!

The book is open and Playland waits

For soldiers and trumpets and little toy trains!

As Folio proceeded through the weird and wild landscape, his whistling voice grew louder and more confident. Dreamland's shadowy images moved aside for him. He grew and changed. His colossal colorful cheer took over the dream. A pathway opened through dark chocolate hills. And golden lantern lights appeared behind the cereal-box buildings – shining through the cutout windows.

The little toy train chugged forward on his wheels, light blue and shiny, stubborn little face with half a smile, now somehow grinning widely.

For Anatole wasn't hiding behind the hills. I wiped my brow in relief. The little boy had seen his train and had procured the ticket. Dreamland tickets were always made of shiny gold paper. They didn't have destinations nor times printed on them, meant to turn in when it was time to go. They were meant for holding, like a friend's hand when you played sing-a-ring-dilly.

"Toot-toot!" sang Folio, and as I watched Anatole's face in his sleep, by the glimmer of the nightlight plugged into the wall, I saw a smile form.

Chug chug, hold on,

Toot toot, sing a tune,

A marching band will cheer for you,

Toys like you, whatever you do,

So, hold on, toot toot, hold on!

Dreamland suddenly transformed. The dark chocolate was swallowed up by other stories Anatole had read. The hundred-acre wood tumbled into a merry-go-round and swirled into a birthday cake. I lost sight of Folio's blue sides. His happy voice chirped like a distant birdy, surprised into yelling. "TOOT!"

I too tumbled, for Anatole had gotten restless. He scrunched while on his stomach, and his knees curled up tight. I rolled and slithered, right up to the fearsome Edge of Bed. I was on my back, and my cap fell off!

I lay like that till morning, too afraid to move. I couldn't look through my spyglass any longer, for Dreamland had faded into misty sleep. Where was brave Folio? I worried while frozen on the Edge. Being frozen too long made a toy go plastic, especially if you were a plastic toy.

It takes a warm hand to wake a frozen toy. And at last the hand scooped me up, and my eyes saw the real world all around me.

"Hurry Anatole!" I heard the boy's mother say. "Get your things! We can't be late to the airport!"

"Grandpa will be on the other side of the plane, right, Mommy?"

"He'll be at the airport in the big city, waiting for us when we land."

"I can't find my toy's cap, Mommy! And his spyglass! And I can't find Folio!"

"You don't need to bother looking for them right now.

You're going to leave your toys here, remember? We can find all the parts when we come back in a few months!"

"No, Mommy, I need my toys! Folio told me so last night in my dreams!"

"Oh really?" His mother indulged him. "What else did Folio say?"

"He said I shouldn't grow up too soon. Is that right, Mommy?"

Her voice carried a lot of love when she answered. Toys in Playland always approved of Mommies.

"That's right, Anatole. Here, let me help you look. There he is! Your toy train was stuck away under your pillow! And here's the cap to your Captain, and his spyglass is inside your train, see? Now, do you have everything you need?"

"Yes! Mommy, will you read to me on the plane? And will Grandpa read to me at bedtime?"

"Yes, dear. Don't worry. The books will stay open as long as you want us to read them!"

Folio and I were placed carefully into Anatole's zipped carryall. We jumbled together upside down, and my cap fell off. But I didn't mind. Back in Playland there was a big celebration. Two marching bands swept up Lieutenant Folio and me. The biggest band was led by Colonel Waistcoat, carrying his fine marching staff with the golden-yellow bauble on the top. It's grand riding on the shoulders of a marching band. I recommend you try it sometime!

Artist's Bio: Pepper's first memories of drawing are of the age of 7 or 8, when she would read a book and create the cover art she envisioned for the story. Throughout her teens and 20's, she would experiment with art on any surface she could find. Painting is her meditation – the only time she can be truly still and completely in the now. She even holds her breath sometimes and has to remind herself to breathe! When she first saw a collection of her work together, she was amazed how much color she used in everything! She loves creating and only wishes she had more time to play and create. It's her happy place. She loves to host paint parties. Pepper sees beauty in everyone's creations and loves to help others experience the joy of completing something and the amazement that they actually created that!

Author's Bio: Victoria Bastedo lives in an old house on the river with a small mountain nearby so she can watch the moon travel over it. She enjoys being in a small town near Seattle, WA; to experience nature at home and also travel to the city to visit the Market and buy the occasional Dicks burger! She's a mother of six children, which has made her by association; a doctor, a teacher, an advice columnist, and a shoulder getting ever more cushioned by time. She has found support in God, her family, and the joy of knowing many friends, including those in her writing group who've given her a lot of help and good advice. Thank you for reading!

Photo: Tara Sreekumar, plentyopixels.com

NORTHBOUND INTERNATIONAL

⊗̂

Cameron Tower & Ellen Rowan

Cameron Tower & Ellen Rowan   Kennedy J. Quinn

Cameron & Ellen's Inspiration: Cameron & Ellen both use found and reclaimed materials to create their work. They decided to build a train, and the pairing with Kennedy's steam train time travel reference sparked some extra gauges and gadgets to be added.

Cameron & Ellen's Partnership: Ellen told Kennedy: Sounds like we are on the same track already! We've been planning what it will look like and would love to show you once we've sketched it out. We have pretty much all of the parts we need. Watch parts, gears, gadgets, stones and keys are right up our alley and my favorite materials with which to create art!

Kennedy's Partnership: Cameron & Ellen were perfect partners. Not only were we in sync, but we're neighbors. I got to see the work in progress. I could not be more delighted with their masterpiece!

Kennedy's Inspiration: The main character of my 5 book series 'always rides a steam train home' when she time travels. So I wanted a reference to Miss Liv Adventures in my story. In the co-op authoring with Sheri J. Kennedy (myself under my other author name and style) a speculative twist was added, and Miss Livingstone went off the rails to consider alternate realities.

DETACHMENT FROM SELF

⊗

Kristin Tetuán

Kristin Tetuán   Sheri J. Kennedy

Kristin's Inspiration: Initially, I had intended some sort of dark train image, but wanting to avoid what was obvious, I settled on a more metaphorical interpretation. By creating a very tormented, confused, tense self-portrait, I am attempting to convey a true sense of loss and perhaps, a bit of struggle to actualize the present moment. In the moment I captured this reference photo, I was truly feeling these things. Early in this pandemic, I had reached a state of disembodiment and disengagement and had some very dark days of self-reflection and chasing the chaotic thought process that ensued as a result, truly, experiencing countless "lost trains of thought".

Kristin's Partnership: Well, due to a technological error, I didn't actually connect with my partner until the last minute! I think it makes for an interesting story, though, considering Sheri's piece explores themes of dementia and alternate realities! That being said, I was able to rely heavily on the amazing support of Deb to get this done and am thrilled to be a part of it.

Sheri's Partnership: I wasn't able to connect with my partner until done. But we both interpreted the theme as a lost train of thought.

Sheri's Inspiration: I often explore unusual mental states or perspectives, so dementia seemed to fit this theme. In the mash up of Kennedy J. Quinn's steam era time travel with my usual reality with a twist style, a speculative edge emerged. It considers dimensions of thought and questions if one could travel to and occupy those dimensions in time travel – the same as any other place and time.

OFF THE RAILS
SPECULATIVE/STEAM ERA TIME TRAVEL
by Sheri J. Kennedy & Kennedy J. Quinn

"His stories are just not rational. He *is* over 90, you know. But he insists he's my father. And though we've been close – especially since he moved in with us following my mother's death – he certainly remains my uncle." Mrs. Scott leaned toward the cocktail tray on the coffee table and poured herself more gin and tonic. When she held the carafe toward her unlikely guest, he raised his half full matching glass with a shake of his head. She settled back onto the impeccable pea-green sofa and crossed her legs. "When he's occasionally lost his place in other fantastical stories, I've been able to talk him back to this reality. But the fact he won't concede I'm not his daughter, no matter how I argue, convinced me to ask your opinion. He doesn't even have a child, or a wife – never did." She shook her head and sighed loudly. "He won't go in to see anyone. And I thought, since you were a friend of the family…"

The young doctor met Mrs. Scott's striking silver-grey eyes, so different from his Marlene's groovy soft amber ones. Although he recognized the same lively spark in her mother's. "I'd be happy to talk with him," he agreed. This could be a cool opportunity to win Mrs. Scott's favor. Finally a break! "Dementia isn't my specialty. But I can give you my opinion." He struggled through one more polite sip of gin.

"That's exactly what I'm looking for, thank you, Barry – or shall I call you, Doctor?" She nodded a close-lipped smile.

Son-in-law perhaps? He could dream. "Barry will do fine," he assured.

"Oh yes, and I suppose we ought to keep your title from Tom anyway. As I said, he's been ornery toward doctors. And he certainly won't take kindly to being doubted. I'd suggest you ask him about history." She stood.

"Uncle, there's a guest to see you," Mrs. Scott called out and waved her drink at the doctor, beckoning him down the short hallway. Barry jumped up and rolled his tongue around his mouth on the way, hoping to ditch the alcohol breath. He had to get it together. The old man was Marlene's relative too. He straightened his sport coat. No use making a bad first impression, even if the old geezer might not remember it.

They ducked from the mod wallpapered hallway into a traditional library. Or Barry thought it was a library. A bed and nightstand stood in one corner, so it was apparently Tom's bedroom. They matched the fruitwood appointments of the ample shelves, and he guessed they were all original to Marlene's great-grandfather's house. He'd never been further in than the entry hall and living room. Now he could see why they'd chosen to move back to Snoqualmie Valley and save the old place. Even though Mrs. Scott's modern decor displayed a different era – and he liked progress – the quality of the home was admirable.

"This is Barry, Barry Locke," Mrs. Scott introduced when her uncle looked up from the open book on his antique writing desk. Barry doubted he'd heard the announcement from the other room. "He, em, is a friend of Marlene's. He'd like to talk with you, Tom." Her eyes darted between the men, and finally rested on Barry.

"Oh, uh, hello. Yes," Barry chimed in. He'd never seen Mrs. Scott nervous before. He cracked up inside and almost forgot to talk. He stuck out his hand toward Tom.

"Pleasure to meet ye, young man." Tom's voice and handshake were warm, and Barry caught himself staring too long into his kind amber eyes. They were remarkably like Marlene's. "I suppose you're here to ask my permission to date my granddaughter," Tom stated.

Barry broke into a wide smile and turned his head to Mrs. Scott. She rolled her eyes and laughed silently, then pulled the door nearly shut as she left. He hoped she mistook his pleasure as agreement with her amusement at her uncle's mistake. Though she seemed perceptive enough to guess Barry wanted her daughter. She'd been sizing him up since they'd met.

"Uh, yes sir," he replied to Tom, "among other things." He remembered his mission and quit talking, to check the man's reactions.

Without missing a beat, Tom asked, "What other things would you be interested in from an old man?"

Barry noted his tight connection to reality. No sign of disorientation, at least currently – dementia could be a tricky thing. "Conversation." He grinned. "Believe it or not, some of us 'kids today' in 'the younger generation' are actually interested in history."

It was Tom's turn to grin. "History's a tangled subject for me. But I guess Marlene thought I'd be a good source for you with all my reading?"

"Yeah, sure." Barry waited to see where old Tom would take it.

"Well why don't you sit in that extra chair there," Tom offered. Barry sat near the desk on the polished wooden chair – well-worn with use. "I could tell you a bunch of facts from what I've read, but you can read for yourself. I'll just share the sources you need. I can tell by your eyes you're a bright fellow – probably finished university – eh?"

"Yes, sir, and graduate studies." He was careful to hide his field but wanted Marlene's great uncle to know his education. The man was unexpectedly sharp; it might take a lot to win him over. Of course Barry had plenty to offer.

"It's the experience of history you gain by talking with a man." Tom stopped and studied Barry's face.

Barry nodded, hoping he'd go on.

Tom apparently took the nod as agreement. "Are you sure that's what you're after?" He cocked a bushy eyebrow at the boy. "I've seen my share of it, to be certain, but my journey's been more complicated than most. I'm not sure you'd want to jump on that train." Tom burst into laughter.

Barry gave an obliging snicker, but the old man's rich laugh grew louder and wilder until he gasped for breath. Barry snickered again but didn't get the joke. Perhaps Tom was a little off after all. Although he certainly appeared with it. Downright quick-witted and healthy.

"Marlene's a wonderful girl," Barry tried. He thought it might help the man get back on track.

"Yes, isn't she though? It's one of the greatest joys of my life to have her near me now. I remember when she was born... but oh, you aren't interested in my personal musings. History, you say." Tom gave two mirthful grunts.

"No please, go on. I'd be happy to know more about her." Barry's eyes glowed, he could feel them. He looked down.

"Mmm, I see. Well, my daughter gave us little hope of a grandchild – but at long last she married. My wife encouraged her to try for a baby right away. It took us many years to conceive, so we worried she might miss her chance. But to our delight, a wee one was on the way before we knew it." Tom stopped. "Is something the matter, boy?" he asked jovially.

"Oh, no sir." Barry snapped shut his gaping mouth and schooled his features to delighted interest. The man was crackers. Both Marlene's grandfathers had died in the first world war. She was always going on about the one who was a hero in Scotland.

"So the time came, and we rushed to the hospital..."

Barry kept nodding but his attention wandered from Tom's story. Mrs. Scott had said Tom never married. And he had no children at all.

"She was the prettiest little thing I ever saw. Spittin' image of her mother as she grew up too, though she has my eyes, of course. I was delighted when my daughter asked me to move here with them after my wife died." Tom smiled and looked as clear as Mrs. Scott's silver-grey gaze. "But I can see I'm boring you now. It was good of you to ask my permission to see her. She's a precious lass. Just what are your intentions toward her,

Barry?"

He even remembered Barry's name. Short-term memory fine. "Uh, serious sir. Though don't tell Mrs. Scott. I mean, it might be better if that's between us men for the time being."

"She doesn't like ye much, is that it?" Thomas laughed freely again. "Just like her mother, she has that way of sizing things up and making up her mind before she considers everything. Not to say she's often wrong." Tom looked Barry over shrewdly. "Is there a reason she's disliking you? No job or..."

"Oh, no sir. I'm... I have a promising career. She... she doesn't like my politics." Barry hesitated, but if he planned to marry Marlene the man would find out sooner or later. "I'm a peacenik, see. I continued my studies partly to avoid the war."

"Ah, and my girl's always supported the military. Her late husband fought in the 2nd War, and she lost her uncle to the Great War. But I'm surprised she'd judge you solely on politics." Tom eyed him again. "He was considered a hero in Scotland, my brother. I myself took employment as a teacher to avoid conscription. I agree this Vietnam is a nasty business. And wishing for a peaceful life is no reason to deny a man love."

"Thank you, sir," Barry smiled and saw Tom's eyes grow deep with sentiment.

"I was denied my love for too long, young Barry. I'll work on my daughter on your behalf. But if she's got something stuck in her craw, she's a stubborn one. At least you can rest assured you've got my blessing on ye. As long as you take care of my granddaughter, and remember, she's my bonnie Marlene as well."

"Uh, yes... yes of course, sir."

"Call me Tom." He stuck out his hand first this time.

"Yes, Tom, thank you." Without knowing what else to say, Barry shook the man's hand and stood to go. "Now that I know you're willing to talk – about history – perhaps we can talk again soon."

"I'd like that," Tom confirmed with a dignified smile. Barry smiled and withdrew.

As he pulled the door ajar behind him, Barry watched the man get back to his reading. Logical and orderly – no sign of dementia there. The doctor nearly skipped down the patterned hallway. He had an ally in the family! Even if the guy was a bit of a kook.

Mrs. Scott leaned forward on the couch and tamped out her cigarette in a crystal ashtray as Barry approached. "So, how is he?" Her gaze fixed on him, as though willing him to agree – with what, he wasn't certain. Did she hope Tom was daft?

"He's certainly sharp enough. Reactions are quick and sensible. No apparent disorientation. He shows understanding of current events." Barry hesitated, leaving out the obvious example of Vietnam. "And memories of past events line up with what I know – such as his brother being a first world war hero in Scotland."

"Mmm," she mused, taking a sip from her refreshed cocktail.

What an idiot. He'd mentioned war heroes after carefully avoiding Vietnam. But she didn't take the bait. She seemed lost in thought. She usually jumped all over him if given the chance.

"Did he tell you any of his personal stories?" she asked, meeting his eye briefly.

"Only about when Marlene was born." Barry cleared his throat. He hadn't really listened to the details and hoped she wouldn't ask about the anecdote. He'd been focused on the facts. Still uncertain what she hoped for, he decided – as a professional – he'd tell her the truth. "There's something odd when it comes to your family." He watched her eyes jump to his and grow keen. "He speaks of you as his daughter, Marlene as his granddaughter, and seems to believe your mother was his wife, just as you said."

"But nothing else? He's well then... otherwise, I mean." She searched his face as if to confirm something.

"As far as I can tell, yes. Although I'm—"

"No expert, yes I know. Thank you for your opinion, Barry. You can see yourself out." She picked up her silver cigarette case and snapped it open, selecting her next victim. Apparently, Barry would be spared for now.

"I can't believe you went and saw her without even telling me." Marlene's amber eyes were like fiery embers. But when she took a sip of her butterscotch malted, Barry was eased; she mustn't be too mad at him. He patted himself on the back for remembering Dairy Freeze was her favorite on sunny evenings.

"You wanted me to get on her good side," he offered. Barry looked up at Mount Si towering over their picnic table, seeking strength to endure her tirade. But nothing came. He checked her face and was met with a relenting grin. "You're the grooviest," he told her with a shake of his head. They beamed at each other.

"So what did you think of Tom?" Her focus returned to her treat.

"It was actually great to talk to him. He gave me permission to date you. It was cool, like—"

"As if I need any man's permission... I'll date any guy I please. And you've got your nerve going along with him. Like I'm his property. Or yours." She rolled her eyes.

"No Marlene, it wasn't... What I mean is, I had to humor him, you know, to get him to talk to me. To check if he was all there."

"And is he?" Her expression was as inscrutable as her mother's.

"Well, he adores the likes of you. So *you* tell *me*," Barry teased. He expected her to laugh and then give away her thoughts. But she just waited, her amber eyes studying his face.

"He seems as sane – perhaps saner – than any old man I've ever met," he continued. "But I guess I'd have to say he's not all there – since he speaks of facts with certainty that the rest of us know to be untrue."

"Mmm, or perhaps not all *here*." Marlene grunted. "Truth is in the eye of the beholder?"

He laughed. "Exactly. I mean, he's right on for the most part. It's only regarding his family..." Barry suddenly remembered, "You know, there was one other thing I found a bit wacky. When we were talking about history, Tom said his personal journey's been more complicated than most, and then he laughed like crazy. He told me I wouldn't want to jump on that train. He was nearly hysterical with the humor of it, but I didn't get what was so funny. Do you know what he's talking about?"

Marlene didn't laugh. She just kept staring toward Barry, evaluating something. At last she said, "Well, thanks for waiting around out here till I was off work." And she dropped her eyes. She gave the last sip of her milkshake a hearty slurp.

"Made my trip from Seattle to see your mom worthwhile," he grinned. But she didn't meet his eye. "Hey, I didn't mean to upset you about Tom." He leaned his head down to the side, trying to get her to look up at him.

"Oh no," she flicked her eyes up to his and then looked around. "I'm not upset. It's just curious, that's all. Perhaps we should do this again next week. And you can stop in to talk with Tom again – ask him about that train?"

"Sure, if you want me to." He waited for more, but she started scooting off the end of the picnic bench. He admired her grace – and her legs – as she stood in her miniskirt without revealing more.

Her mom was sitting in a tall-backed wooden chair on the wide porch when Barry and Marlene pulled up in his blue-green corvette. Marlene jumped out quickly and dismissed him with a wave and a smile. As he turned around on the drive, he waved and shouted, "See you soon, Mrs. Scott." She acknowledged him with a close-lipped nod.

Marlene was amazed. Things were looking up.

"Hey mom, how'd it go today?" Marlene asked as she hopped up the steps to the porch.

"I tested him, just like I told you I should. Barry's observations were brief and lingered on surface things." Mrs. Scott tamped out her cigarette.

"Yeah, you were right about that part. But I wish you would have told me you were going through with it. Anyway, I figured we'd better finish the test. Give him one more chance. I asked Barry to come back and talk to Tom some more next week."

Mrs. Scott got up and followed her daughter into the house.

Barry tipped the gin and tonic glass to his closed lips and set it on the coaster on the coffee table again. He really needed to get Marlene to hip her mother to his distaste for the cocktail scene. She'd know how to break it to her without messing up his progress with her mother.

"So good of you to be willing to talk with Tom again," Mrs. Scott said.

"My pleasure," he nodded. Though he couldn't see much use in it. The guy already liked him, and he already told them what they needed to know. So what's the big deal? Why did Marlene and her mom want him to do this? At least he might find out what was so damn funny about the train.

He followed Mrs. Scott down the mod hall, same as last time. When they entered Tom was sitting in the same chair at his desk and came to attention when they entered, in the same way. And Mrs. Scott pulled the door nearly closed as she left, just as before. It was like going back in time except for the book Tom looked up from was different.

"Nice to see ye again, young Barry," Tom greeted with a smile.

Barry noted Tom remembered his name without reintroduction. "Yes. Good to see you, Tom. I'm back to hear some of that tangled history you were mentioning. I guess I'm ready to hop on that train." He snickered with a nod.

To Barry's surprise Tom regarded him without the slightest crinkle of amusement. Tom's searching stare lasted so long, Barry's usual confidence squirmed from him. He looked down at his hands and shifted from foot to foot next to the writing desk.

"This was your idea was it?" Tom asked.

Barry glanced up, down, then met Tom's soft amber eyes. "Actually, sir, it was Marlene's." He looked off at the bright window by the bed.

"Well, aye then, she's wanting me to tell you of our... unexpected journeys. How I met my, Lizzie, is a good place to start. Especially since I know you're interested in courting your young lass about now. As I told you my love was a long time coming, and it was a near miss too." Tom held out a hand toward the two traditional leather lounge chairs across the room and stood.

The two men shuffled over to settle in as Tom went on. "Marlene's grandmother was a wily lass. Broke into my bookshop once, just down the way from here in Snoqualmie. That was when I was a young man – just arrived from Scotland. It's gone now, of course, along with my partner, Mr. Manush. The man was undeniably strange, and my Lizzie got pulled into a world of trouble thanks to a secret set of stone amulets – gems they were – that she found in his odd cabinet in the back of the store. The stones had powers. When you touched them, they moved you instantly through time or space or both." Tom sat, and Barry sat back into the chair across from him. Sounded like it would be a long absurd tale. But Barry had to wait around for Marlene to get off work anyway. He tuned in for the ride.

"When Lizzie found the stones, there were some missing from the tray, and she and my brother Scott fell hard to chasing their mystery. Each had a different property, and they believed if they gained them all, they could master Time."

"But didn't you say this was about your love life?" Barry asked. They didn't have all day.

"I'm getting to that. Don't you fret. But it won't make sense without the rest of the story."

Barry stifled a guffaw. Like this nonsense could make any sense at all? "Go on," he urged.

"So Scott, my brother, was sweet on Lizzie too. And he lured her attention from me with his daring and charm. They whisked away together using the stone's powers of affinity, hither and thither across the world and back and forth through time. But Lizzie told me that no matter where she roamed, she could always take a steam train home. So I waited here, in my shop by the depot, under the mountain's beauty." Tom gazed at the window, like he could see the mountain there, though it loomed in a different direction.

"We became the dearest of friends. I kept my shop, always near the train. And she came to me, time and time again. Until one day we parted. I watched her marry my brother and go away to live in Scotland. She longed to have a daughter – Marlene's mother, I suppose. I was heart-broken, to be certain, for I'd always hoped her child would also be my own. I lived in regret – that I'd never told her of my love for her. For I loved her in truth." Tom paused, and Barry nodded for him to continue.

"After many a long year, I moved my shop to Boston – knowing she kept touch there with her family's home. She'd told me once that she saw me briefly in my bookshop there – in 1941 – on one of her first time travel journeys. It was when she snuck into my shop and used a stone, before she'd even met me here in Snoqualmie in 1910. So I established my new shop in

Boston near the train station. And I waited for her to come from Snoqualmie 1910 to Boston in 1941. It's a strange thing, Time. That I could wait so long for her to do what she once had done."

"You can say that again," Barry agreed. "But why would you do all that just to see her briefly and so young, before she even knew you? Wouldn't that just be torture, if you knew she was going to marry your brother?"

Tom smiled at the young man across from him perched on the edge of his chair. "Torturous indeed if I didn't have hope. But since I knew the day and place of her arrival, I met her there instead of waiting for her to find me. When at last she arrived, I changed things. I spent time with her and showed her my affection. I told her I wanted things to be different. I could see I'd captured her heart, but there was nothing I could do but wait some more. When she left back to Snoqualmie 1910, to meet me again and travel on her strange journeys, I hoped against hope that the twist I'd added would bring her home to me once and for all." He paused.

"And did it?" Barry couldn't help his curiosity.

"I was much older than she, and it was a chance for my younger self that I created that time around. In another time dimension. For my twist created a split, of course. My honesty changed that young Lizzie and gave her a chance to choose again."

Tom fell silent. Gazing at the window where golden sunlight played in rippling patterns on the sheer curtain's veil. Barry stared at the eerie bands of light, like the rippling dimensions of time.

"So you saw her young again? You witnessed her travel through time?" The old man seemed to believe it so fully, Barry was sucked in – at least to consider if this was evidence.

"Yes, for the first time I saw it remarkably proven true, before my eyes. But I believed her from the start."

"Wait, you never saw it happen before you moved your books all the way to Boston? You waited all those years on faith? You just trusted she would be there?" Barry's mouth hung open.

"I trusted *her*," Tom stated simply. "And that's what matters." He stared off at the window, apparently done with his story.

Barry checked his Rolex, and the submariner seemed to have taken an uncanny leap forward in time. He laughed to himself. It was time to pick up Marlene. "Uh, thanks for the story, Tom. I'm afraid it's time to go." Barry hopped from the chair.

"Haste ye back." Tom turned with a nod to Barry and then returned to gazing at the sunlit window.

"So, how'd it go with my mom today," Marlene asked Barry when they'd settled at the picnic table near the foot of the mountain. In the car, Barry had offered nothing but small talk about her job.

"She was as mysterious as ever," Barry quipped.

"What's that supposed to mean?" Marlene rolled her eyes and laughed.

"You know how she is. She just drinks and smokes and looks at me across the coffee table. It's like she's waiting for me to mess up or something."

"Well, you don't expect her to let her incredible daughter

date just anybody, do you?" she teased.

"Oh, come on," Barry defended. "I'm a doctor from a good family. I'm popular and..."

"Witty and handsome," she added with a giggle.

"And isn't that good enough for her?" His tone was serious.

Marlene sobered too. "There's more to life than credentials, Barry."

"So it *is* my politics. I'm not going to go try to be a war hero just to impress your mom," he insisted.

"I think you're missing the point," Marlene said. "I—"

"Oh, and before I forget. Unless it will deeply offend her, can you get her to lay off the formal cocktail service when I visit? It's so bourgeois."

"Of course," Marlene agreed. "She won't care if you're not into all that. How'd it go with Tom?"

"Wow, it was far out." He laughed. "Not in the groovy sense, I mean really out there. He told me the wildest story about your grandmother. Or wait, your great-aunt. He's got me confused. Or actually, he never got around to telling me about his marriage. He told me about his brother Scott's wife and how he wished he'd told her that he loved her when they were all young."

"Uh huh, my grandfather Scott. Or my great-uncle if you live in old Tom's inner-dimension – the one in his mind."

"Exactly. Did he ever tell you the part about waiting for Lizzie in 1941 to add a twist and start her all over in 1910, but in another dimension?"

"Of course. That's the best part... well almost. Tom is so

dear." She beamed.

"Dearly delusional," Barry said and laughed, beaming back at her.

Marlene's face fell. "You don't believe him?"

"Of course not." Tom shook his head.

"But he's telling the truth." For all the world, Marlene looked totally serious. "I've heard these types of stories all my life from my mom and my grandmother. Time travel is part of my legacy."

"Marlene..." Barry didn't know what to say.

"Don't you believe me?" Her soft amber eyes pleaded with Barry.

He didn't want to let her go. "It's an awful lot to take in," he tried. "I'm a man of science, an intellectual. I study facts and build my beliefs on observations. My reputation, my politics..."

"Have you observed me to be a liar?" Such a question, she usually would have delivered with fiery verve, but her tone washed over Barry as gently as the evening breeze caressing his face.

He hesitated. Gazing up at the mountain, lit golden above the valley, he remembered Tom's words, 'I trusted *her.*'

When they arrived in the corvette, Marlene's mom was sitting in the tall-backed wooden chair on the wide porch again. Marlene and Barry got out of the car. "Hi Mom," Marlene shouted.

Mrs. Scott waved and tipped her head with a guarded smile.

Marlene bounded up the steps ahead of Barry. "We're going in to hear the rest of Tom's story together," she told her mom, with a glowing smile. She went inside.

"So good to see you, Barry," Mrs. Scott smiled, and her silvery eyes melted with warmth.

"Uh, yeah, thanks for having me," Barry fumbled. He was taken off guard by her welcome. He followed Marlene into the house.

Marlene kicked off her shoes on the hardwoods by the door. "Come on," she urged him.

Barry followed suit, then caught up with Marlene. They padded across the thick shag carpet of the living room and down the mod hall beyond. With a light rap of knuckles, Marlene pushed open the door to Tom's room. "Mind if we join you?" She indicated Barry behind her.

Tom's smile showed his delight, and he moved from his desk to one of the leather lounge chairs in the corner. Barry grabbed the extra wooden chair and brought it over next to Tom. The aged man patted the seat of the chair across from him, and Marlene sat down as he wished. "Marlene, lass. What brings you to see your old grandfather? Are you checking on what this young man of yours learned from me about you? I told him only good things – not that there's much bad to be finding. And I'm all for making him part of the family."

"Uncle Tom!" she burst. "You didn't tell him to marry me, did you? How embarrassing. We haven't even spoken of—" She turned to Barry with a deep blush.

"It wasn't my idea, I assure you," Tom said. Her mouth fell open and his bushy brow fell to worry.

"So he told you he wants to marry...?" Her shocked face

THE LOST TRAIN ⊗ ANTHOLOGY

shined. And her eyes stole sideways at Barry.

"Well not in so many words. He was asking to court you – with serious intent. But why'd you call me Uncle Tom? The boy came to ask me for your hand, as your grandfather, didn't he?" Tom stared off at the window. The sheer curtains glowed, luminous as a lingering spirit in the evening light.

"Of course," Marlene confirmed with full verve. "You know I get mixed up sometimes. Forgive me?"

"I suppose I get mixed up sometimes myself," Tom agreed with a laugh. "I told you it's a tangled history," he said to Barry.

"Indeed," Marlene agreed. And they all laughed together.

"So, Uncle Grandfather, Barry said you told him about the old days, and the twist. But can you tell us the rest? The story of the inner-dimension and how you and my grandmother got together?"

"Ah yes, the best part." He smiled. "Everyone likes a happy ending."

Barry marveled in the segue from the talk of their love life to Tom's. Marlene wanted to marry him. He believed anything was possible!

Tom said, "It's one of your favorites, I know." His amber eyes twinkled at Marlene, and she responded with a sparkling smile.

"So when my Lizzie left me, in 1941, I hoped against hope she would come again. But I understood the Lizzie that knew of my love for her lived in a different time period from where I dwelled. I found comfort in knowing that my young self might find love. But I was still alone."

Marlene grabbed the old man's hand. And he sighed and

gave her a grim grin. She let go and sat back with an encouraging nod to go on.

"But even with such odds against it, I kept hope she'd come to me across the dimensions of time and space, and we'd be together before I passed on."

Tom stopped, gazing again at the window, and Barry's eyes followed to the light.

Marlene kicked her chair absently, waiting for Tom to continue. She knew the rest, of course, but Barry didn't. Barry shifted in his chair, curious again, and finally their movements brought Tom's attention back to the story.

"Your grandmother," he said to Marlene, "my dear Lizzie, told me often of the many other journeys she chose, but she always wondered if ours was meant to be? For though she'd used the stones hoping to find me on our momentous day, she at first had no success. My shop in Boston had changed, and I wasn't in when she arrived. She left upset, and climbed aboard at the nearby station to ride the steam train home to 1910. When the train was moving, she contacted her gem and arrived at Snoqualmie Depot, as had happened before. But as she stepped off the train, toward the platform, her ankle turned on the steps and she fell and hit her head. She lost consciousness."

"Was she alright?" Barry asked. Marlene took his hand this time, and he met her reassuring eyes.

"I was sitting here – right here – upon an evening, thinking and staring out the window into the light. I lost my train of thought, and there she was. Or should I say, 'here she was'." He pointed to his temple. "Our lost trains of thought collided in a place beyond time, an inner-dimensional space, and our whole prior lives jumped the track together, my Lizzie's and mine." Old Tom's face caught the light and his face shined at Marlene and Barry. "And here we are now – home at last."

Mrs. Scott came back from the kitchen with a nice cold beer for Barry. He noted it was still in the perfect glass – a frosted mug. He took a sip and admitted, "Delicious." He smiled at Marlene where she sat with legs curled up, next to him on the pea-green sofa. Mrs. Scott took the chair, and she poured Marlene and herself a gin and tonic.

"So, Barry," she said, "do you still think Tom is losing it?" Her silver-grey eyes rested on him, waiting.

"Do you want his professional or personal opinion, Mom?" Marlene asked.

Barry spoke up before she could answer. "Tom is a good man." He paused and then smiled. "He kept his faith and he's found his love. And that's what matters."

Mrs. Scott raised her glass. "To Marlene and Barry!" she toasted.

They all clinked glasses and laughed together.

Artist's Bio: Born in Racine, WI in 1967, Cameron Tower was raised around art museums and art shows. He discovered he was an artist through drawing in 5th grade. He studied drawing and painting in college and metalworking for 7 years at Schwinn Bicycle Company. He moved to the PNW in 1993 to study flameworking and to the Seattle area in 1998 to work at the Glass Eye and Glassybaby. He designed and created functional glass art and learned how to mig weld as a technician at the Glass Eye. He then designed and created tools for glass artists and studios. Cam is an independent artist and craftsman who recently moved his home and studio to North Bend. He creates functional glass art, welded metal tools and sculptures. He also builds structures using found, rescued wood and other materials. He loves using high temperature materials to create more functional beautiful objects and mechanisms in the world.

Artist's Bio: Ellen Rowan is a prolific artist inspired by the natural beauty around her and is passionate about sustainability. She creates art from rocks, metal, wood and other rescued objects. Her artistic expressions include intricate mandalas, unique functional art and wearable art pendants. She's been active in the Snoqualmie Valley art community for over 20 years and is deeply connected with local artists. As a board member of North Bend Art and Industry she's excited about spreading awareness of the vision of NBA&I, and thrilled to teach different forms of art and develop a collaborative creative environment for people of all ages and backgrounds. Ellen worked throughout her teens with children and troubled youth, using art as play and therapy. She's worked as a marketing and social media consultant for the last 12 years. Ellen holds majors in Art and Psychology, Wittenberg University, Masters in Education with School Counseling Certification, Seattle Pacific University.

Author's Bio: Kennedy J. Quinn is an adventurer who loves to weave images gathered on life's travels into artworks and mosaics of words. She has written seven novels and lives with her husband in North Bend, Washington on the banks of the Snoqualmie River. She is a.k.a. Sheri J. Kennedy. She was a picture framer for 18 years and enjoyed a successful visual arts career. Although an introvert, she was a radio DJ in University. In recent years, Kennedy has been writing a 5 book series, *The Unwitting Journey's of the Witty Miss Livingstone*, or *Miss Liv Adventures* for short. The twists and turns of steam era time travel are a fun challenge for her. Books 1 & 2 are published, and book 3 is scheduled for release in fall of 2020.

Artist's Bio: Kristin Tetuán is an arts educator, performing and visual artist, photographer and entrepreneur. She's an active arts advocate and hopes to grow her pet project, Art Club., into an organization that makes career-focused arts more accessible to underserved and marginalized groups. She's passionate about bringing attention to alternative path learners through this advocacy. By attempting to put the "college degree = success" myth to rest and by getting involved in projects like Lost Train, she hopes to set an example for others like herself – to trail-blaze a path for alt path learners in the creative professional world.

Author's Bio: Sheri J. Kennedy a.k.a. Kennedy J. Quinn is an individual who thrives on creating. She's a visual artist, photographer and writer. *Feeling Human* is her fifth novel. She studied philosophy, literature and communications and earned a B.A. in Humanities. Most of her writing starts with exploration of an idea and speculates on alternate perspectives which she calls, Reality with a Twist. Thoughtful curiosity influences all of her pursuits. She enjoys participation in her community and life with her husband in a small house on the banks of the Snoqualmie River near Seattle, Washington. Sheri is owner of FreeValley Publishing / FVP Books and Editor of FVP's website. She's also an insurance agent. She actively pursues her career as an author, as well as encouraging others in FVP's cooperative author group.

TAKEN BY NATURE

⊗

Stefanie Allison

Stefanie Allison Rachel Barnard

Stefanie's Inspiration: 'The Lost Train,' when I first read the title for the Anthology, I thought of an abandoned overlooked train caboose. Lost to everyday life, being devoured by nature. I chose to draw my art because it embraces the unremembered, the forgotten train car.

Stefanie's Partnership: Stefanie told Rachel: I cannot wait to read your work. I will be inking 7 versions with plant life native to North Bend. A broke down decaying train on tracks in the middle of nowhere, as nature grows in an around uniting a metal object to the foliage of nature.

Rachel's Partnership: Rachel enjoyed collaborating with Stefanie. Rachel was delighted to include some of the flora Stefanie chose into the short story and ground the setting with identifiable PNW plants. One of Rachel's hobbies is foraging and plant identification. She enjoyed researching all the ferns and other local plants that Stefanie drew and asking, how could the main character use this plant?

Rachels's Inspiration: SAVOUR is literally a lost train car but the story dives much deeper into the loss of a treasure and source of income. This short story was directly inspired by Rachel's fascination with tiny houses and tiny living. The emotions of the characters and the mood of the piece were influenced by the grief that is being felt all over the world right now over loss of income, loss of stability, and loss of freedom.

SAVOUR
MYSTERY
by Rachel Barnard

Jackson stared in shock at the empty tracks. The railroad ties, shadowed for years, were covered in moss, and glistening with morning dew. One of the twin oak ferns that normally guarded each side of the train car was trampled, several of the proud stems twisted and broken. A footprint dusted across one large downed leaf.

Jackson followed the twin lines etched in the dirt into the forest with his eyes, his mouth agape. His legs automatically traced their path, wending around his property and ending in deeper divots in front of the street before disappearing into the pavement. Gone.

His first thought, after the shock of empty air above the carefully placed train tracks had passed, was not that a thief had absconded with their Airbnb. It was not that their main source of income had vanished overnight. Nor did he think about the journalist that had booked the converted train car for next week. No, the first thought Jackson had was regret for the lost prized rack decorating the outside of the car.

Jackson was not a hunter, but he and his wife, Marcie, owned over five acres of private land in North Bend. They often walked their backyard and the day Jackson proposed to Marcie, they had stumbled upon the first antler. He had asked if she would marry him, then and there. "Three points!" he'd declared. Not more than a yard away they'd found the matching antler and Marcie had said, "yes! It's a sign." Antlers three feet apart. Their relationship three years old. They were married in that same spot nine months later.

On their first anniversary they'd sourced an abandoned train car and built the converted tiny house, placing it on roughly the same spot they'd found the antlers. On Airbnb they listed it as the Stunning Accommodation with a View, Off-grid, Unique, and Relaxing converted train car. SAVOUR for short.

Jackson dragged himself back to the forlorn train tracks laying lonely without purpose. He bent down to inspect the tracks. Up close he noticed visible scuffs from the theft. Shoved behind one of the railroad ties, he spotted a piece of wood. He carefully pulled it free from the dirt that loosely covered one corner. The cheery teal paint on the reclaimed wood had faded from five years' use. He turned it around with a sigh, knowing the words he'd see before he could read them. *Savour the little things.*

His knees dropped to the ground and the welcome board slid back into the dirt. Jackson stared up at the trees. The wind whispered questions through the leaves. Who took SAVOUR and why? How could he tell Marcie?

The trudge from the empty tracks back to the house, just an acre, felt like an eternity. Jackson clutched the abandoned sign under his arm and bore down on a grimace. His shoulders drooped and a dull ache gripped the back of his neck.

"Jacksy, is that you?" Marcie's cheerful voice floated through the screen door which let in air but kept out spring insects.

As if sensing the disturbance and despair rolling off Jackson, Marcie met him at the door. Her face fell when she spotted him.

"Jackson?" she whispered.

"It's gone." Jackson held out the sign, reading it again as Marcie took it from his rigid fingers. *Savour the little things.*

"Gone? Even..." Marcie trailed off as she took the sign from him and set it down on the table next to their car keys and other odds and ends.

Jackson nodded. They both knew she meant the pair of deer antlers.

Marcie reached up and they embraced. Jackson felt the burden of the loss shared equally between them. Warmth from Marcie pushed into his chest and he sagged in her arms. They held each other for a long moment before letting go.

"Nick and Sheila," Marcie said suddenly. "Should we tell them not to come?"

Jackson shook his head. The antlers they'd had for six years. The train car Airbnb for five. But they'd had their monthly game night with their neighbors to the north longer still. Every month for seven years Nick and Sheila brought a bottle of red wine on odd months and a bottle of white wine on even months for game night.

"Are you still up for it?" Jackson asked Marcie.

She nodded, but the pallor of her face suggested otherwise.

"Hello Neighbors!" Nick and Sheila called together through the open door from a few feet behind Jackson.

Jackson swiveled in the narrow hall space to greet them. Marcie's hand settled on his shoulder. The warmth strengthened him, making him feel a touch more like himself. He schooled his features into a neutral expression but as soon as Nick saw him, he asked, "Something the matter?"

Jackson noted the bottle Sheila carried was their current favorite, the 2017 limited release Chenin Blanc, from their local Woodinville winery, Chateau Ste Michelle. "I'm going to need some of that," he said to no one in particular.

"What's wrong with Jackson?" Sheila asked Marcie, who still hovered behind him.

"The carriage is missing," she answered with a shrug, as if she didn't believe it.

"What? Your Airbnb?" Nick asked.

"SAVOUR?" Sheila added.

Jackson nodded. "Nothing but empty track."

"Let's go check it out," Nick urged.

Jackson nodded again. Marcie's hand slid from his shoulder to grasp his hand and they joined Sheila and Nick on the porch – the forgotten welcome sign clutched in Marcie's other hand.

Jackson led them back the way he'd come, to the glaringly empty spot where the carriage should have been. His eyes were drawn once again to the telltale marks showing the train car had been wheeled away through the dirt.

"I thought the wheels didn't work?" Nick asked, bending down to inspect the twin lines.

"They did," Jackson said. "Remember Savannah and Darion helped me fix them last season," he added.

"Oh, that's right," Nick mused.

"What are you going to do?" Sheila asked. She still clutched the wine bottle in her hand.

Jackson didn't answer right away.

"Oh, what about that journalist? Isn't she supposed to come later this week?" Sheila asked.

"Is anyone else booked?" Nick asked.

"Oh gosh!" Marcie said, looking toward Jackson as panic grew behind her eyes. "We'll have to cancel."

Jackson hadn't forgotten the journalist, but his mind was preoccupied trying to grasp the reality of what wasn't in front of him.

"That's the least of your worries. Someone stole your caboose," Nick said with a shake of his head.

"Who would do such a thing?" Sheila exclaimed.

They marched back to the house in silence. Marcie opened and poured the bottle of wine immediately after they entered. Jackson plopped into a seat at the dining room table. Nick clapped him on the back reassuringly.

"Do you think it was someone who stayed in SAVOUR?" Marcie asked when they sat with full glasses in front of each of them.

"Very likely. Who else knows where to find the carriage?"

Sheila asked.

"Just the journalist and the neighbors," Marcie said with a shrug.

Jackson took a long pull of wine, letting the flat texture of the liquid coat his tongue before he swallowed.

"I'll make a list of everything we'll have to do. Jackson?" Marcie said.

"Hm?"

"Can you make a list of everyone who stayed in SAVOUR for the past month?"

"Better make it the last 6 months, or since whenever you started telling people the wheels worked," Nick added.

Jackson nodded absently, thinking again about the antlers and how Marcie hadn't yet mentioned their loss.

"Are you going to report it?" Nick asked.

Jackson shook his head to clear away the fog in his brain.

"Really? When Darion's Trek was stolen, he reported it right away," Nick said. His mouth formed a hard-lined grimace. "If the police don't know your property was stolen, they can't get it back to you when they find it. Do you have insurance?"

Marcie nodded, worrying her bottom lip. She blinked rapidly as if keeping tears at bay. Jackson wanted to soothe her, but he felt glued to his chair. He took another gulp of wine, barely tasting it.

"Good," Nick said. "We didn't have insurance on Darion's bike or we could have made a claim. Two thousand down the drain and Darion had to ride public transportation for the rest of the year until he could afford to buy a car."

"Didn't know you could get insurance for a bike," Marcie said softly.

"Bikes are often stolen. Especially electronic bikes," Sheila said.

"Turns out Savannah borrowed the bike without asking." Nick shook his head ruefully.

"And then she left it at a friend's, and it disappeared," Sheila said, tsking. "It's too bad she didn't tell us sooner."

"How is Savannah?" Marcie asked.

The normal conversation buzzed around Jackson like white noise. He sipped his wine, tilting his head back to catch the last drops. Marcie scooted a second opened bottle of wine to him.

"You know Savannah," Sheila chuckled.

"Always getting into trouble, especially since finishing college last year," Nick said.

"And Darion?" Marcie asked.

Jackson uncorked and poured himself a hefty second glass. He offered the bottle to Nick who shook a hand over his half-full glass. Sheila held hers aloft and Jackson refilled her glass.

"Unlike Savannah, Darion has always been more studious, and we don't worry about him finishing Uni," Nick said.

"He's got two years left, right? We were glad to hear Savannah graduated," Marcie replied.

Sheila sighed and shared a look with Nick before replying. "We were worried when she switched from photography to philosophy but she made it."

"Darion's studying criminal justice and psychology," Nick

added.

"Oh!" Sheila said and Jackson jumped inwardly beside her. "Perhaps Darion could help you profile your recent guests."

"That's a great idea!" Marcie smiled at Jackson hopefully, and he nodded automatically.

Jackson cleared his throat and pushed back from the table. "I'm going to compile that list."

Sheila and Nick started to stand up.

"No, no, don't get up. Marcie made her famous apple pie. I'd hate for that to go to waste. It's been a comfort having you both here, and I'm sorry we didn't actually get to gaming tonight."

"Don't apologize," Nick said, and Sheila nodded, settling back in her chair.

"I'll send what I have for Darion to take a look at as soon as I get it all together," Jackson said.

He nodded to the three of them and backed out of the dining room, heading to their office. Jackson and Marcie never had kids, so they'd converted the larger guest room into a home office. It featured an enormous desk that was topped with a unique Walnut slab atop four steel motorized legs. Jackson powered up his laptop, adjusting the height of the desk so he could stand. He was too jittery to sit – from the wine and the task at hand.

After compiling the list of every guest that had stayed at SAVOUR since the wheels were repaired, he went into each profile and pulled all the information he could. He copied the messages for each guest into a separate document and jotted down any other information he could find about them. Several profiles stood out and he put those at the top before sending the file to Darion along with an explanation of the disappearance.

The most suspicious guest was the most recent couple to spend time in SAVOUR – just two days ago. It hadn't struck him at the time, but when he'd given them a tour of the grounds, they'd been especially interested in the mechanics of the wheels and how he'd gotten them to function.

"We are simply fascinated by the Colonial railcars. We tried to get our hands on our own caboose from Amtrak, but were outbid," Mr. Smith said.

"And how did you get the car onto your property?" Mrs. Smith asked.

Jackson proudly explained the ordeal of moving the caboose and getting it situated permanently on their property. "It was much easier to get the licensing and permits to operate it as a rental property than it was to move it from our local scrapyard. And we were lucky they had one! Although it was in such a state of disrepair that it took months to restore."

"Amazing! You did a fine job," Mrs. Smith said.

Mr. Smith leaned down closer to inspect the wheels. "Tell me again about that wheel mechanism and how you locked it to this piece of track?"

Jackson printed off his list with accompanying documentation and pulled the sheaf of papers from the printer still warm.

When he returned, Marcie was alone in the kitchen washing the wine glasses. A medium-sized slice of apple pie sat on a dessert plate on the counter beside the sink. She gestured to the treat and smiled hesitantly at him. He set the papers next to the pie and walked up behind her. "We'll find our caboose," he murmured into the back of her hair as he held her close. She settled into him and sighed, her hands loosely resting on the edge of the sink.

She turned to face him and wiped her hands dry on a dish towel. "And what if we don't?" Her eyes loomed large with worry.

"We'll find it."

Two days passed quickly after filing the police report. Darion had agreed to evaluate the communications and reports on the recent guests but had come up with nothing significant. Jackson and Marcie sat on their porch and sipped their morning coffee, staring despondently toward the forest and their lost train.

"It's time to cancel the journalist," Marcie said gently. "It's too bad we'll miss out on the exposure from her story."

Jackson nodded and grabbed his cell phone. Before he could dial the number, the phone jingled in his hands and he accepted the call, putting it on speaker so they could both hear.

"Hello, Jackson? This is your insurance agent Chad. We spoke briefly several days ago when I gave you the info to put in the claim for the theft of your tiny house?"

"Um, yes," Jackson said.

"I just heard from the adjuster, and I wanted to explain personally. Unfortunately, your standard homeowner's insurance doesn't cover this type of property theft. You had the endorsement for Airbnb rental liability, but because you didn't construct it using a certified builder, we were not able to insure the tiny-home structure. We did discuss this several years ago. I'm very sorry. Is there anything else I can do for you?"

Jackson sighed and didn't respond. Marcie leaned over the phone. "No, thank you Chad."

"Okay then, you two take care."

Marcie pressed end. Jackson sighed again and pinched his eyes closed. He didn't recall any sort of conversation details about insuring the tiny house when they'd finished building. He just remembered his agent scolding him about how he should have called before building it.

A light breeze floated through the trees, murmuring its consolation.

"I was reading about how common this is," Marcie said. "Apparently, there's no tracking stolen homes. No database, I mean. But because they're on wheels, it happens more than you'd think."

Jackson nodded but didn't respond. They should have looked into specialty insurance. They should have worked with a builder instead of remodeling themselves. Marcie rubbed his shoulders and he leaned into her touch.

"We don't have to call the journalist right now," Marcie said.

"Let's just get it over with." He quickly pulled up the contact and hit the call button, putting the phone on speaker.

"Denise speaking."

"Hi Denise. This is Marcie and Jackson." He looked at Marcie as he spoke.

"Great to hear from you," Denise said.

"Right, well, this is difficult for us to do but we have to cancel your stay in the SAVOUR carriage," Jackson kept his tone even.

"Oh?"

"We would love to be featured in your article and we were really looking forward to the exposure," Marcie added.

Denise didn't say anything, so Jackson pressed on, pulling the words out like rotten teeth. "The carriage was stolen last week. We're not sure if it's going to turn up or what condition it'll be in if it is found."

"Really?" Denise drew out the word as if each letter was a question. "I'm truly sorry for the loss. From the pictures you sent, it was a great caboose with a lot of history, and you put in significant time and effort restoring it. Unfortunately, my list of top ten unique places to stay in the Pacific Northwest can only include current listings, so I won't be able to include SAVOUR in that feature if it is truly lost." Denise paused. "But I already have my flight booked to Seattle. Can I explore this story? I'd like to write about it if you'd be willing to tell me more. Care to elaborate?"

Jackson let out the breath he hadn't realized he was holding. Marcie grabbed hold of his hand and whispered, "I'm game if you are. Perhaps we can turn this around."

"Okay, Denise. We'd love to have you. We can only provide the guest loft in our house if you'd like to stay on the property. Otherwise there's a local log cabin B&B or several local motels," Jackson said.

"Don't trouble yourselves with the accommodations. I'm sure I can find plenty of suitable possibilities in North Bend.

Exploring local is my specialty."

Jackson could hear the smile behind Denise's words.

"Lovely," Marcie said, her face brighter. "We're still available anytime Friday for your interview and you're welcome to photograph the grounds."

"That would be very helpful. If you have any questions don't hesitate to call prior to Friday, but if not, I will see you around nine in the AM?" Denise suggested.

"Yes, we'll see you then. Thanks, Denise," Jackson said.

"Bye see you soon," Marcie added.

Jackson ended the call and turned to Marcie, letting out another sigh.

"That went better than I thought it would," Marcie said with a short uncomfortable laugh.

Her words echoed the day after they had their first paying guest:

"That went better than I thought it would," Marcie said, glancing around at the ground in front of SAVOUR.

Trash was scattered amidst the littered pinecones.

"Remind me to say 'no' next time they ask about how secluded this place is," Jackson muttered, stooping down to pick up an errant cigarette butt.

"Not everyone is like this," Marcie said as she too picked up a wayward piece of paper.

Jackson continued muttering as he set about cleaning up the train car's 'front lawn.' "We should increase our cleaning fee," he said.

"Jackson!" Marcie exclaimed and he jumped.

"What is it?"

"Check this out." Marcie held out the piece of paper, now unfolded and nearly the size of her palm.

On the paper was a drawing of their train car, clearly identified by the large twin antlers and the words, "She flies with her own wings." Surrounding the train car, nearly suffocating it, were small groupings of the ghost plant Indian-pipe.

"Neat. I'll put this with the lost treasures." Jackson opened the door and stepped inside the tiny house.

He was always surprised at how spacious it seemed on the inside, like taking a larger breath than he thought possible. Smiling, he stepped over to the small music box sitting on the windowsill and opened it. Their neighbors – Sheila and Nick – had given this children's plaything to them as a joke on their first anniversary.

The couple had stayed in SAVOUR with their two teenagers once before it was opened to Airbnb. Since the train car only featured a single queen bed, Nick and Sheila convinced Savannah and Darion to sleep in a tent outside.

In retribution for the gag gift, Jackson and Marcie had set up the music box in the carriage the night before Nick and Sheila had stayed, and it had remained there ever since. The music box, when opened, featured a placard stating it was for lost items and things left behind either by accident or on purpose.

Denise peered at the empty tracks, then left and right as if searching for evidence of the missing caboose being dragged over the dirt.

"It's rained," Jackson said, kicking at one of the many pinecones.

Denise nodded, pursing her lips. She scratched behind an ear and then strode off into the woods.

"The tracks didn't lead that way," Marcie said.

"Oh? And did you check all the surrounding area? And how many pounds did you say the carriage was?"

"A lot. More than 5 tons," Jackson told her.

"We did check in every direction," Marcie piped up from behind Jackson. She came forward.

Nodding again, Denise walked back toward them and sat down on one of the log chairs that surrounded the fire pit. She pulled out a pad and pen and wrote something down. "And you mentioned the police already cleared several of the recent occupants?"

Marcie nodded and Jackson said, "We spoke with one of the police detectives yesterday after giving them all the information that Darion, our neighbor's son, put together. The Smiths, a nice older couple fascinated with trains, were outside the country the week our carriage disappeared. Most of the people who book us are from out of town, actually."

"Mmhmm." Denise scribbled away before peering back up at them. "I know this is hard and the lack of information must be most infuriating. Can you tell me more about the significance of SAVOUR and why the train car is so important to you?"

"We're a part of the FIRE community," Marcie said.

"Financial Independence Retire Early," Jackson added. "It's

a movement just like it sounds."

Marcie nodded at his comment and told Denise, "we were only able to retire at our age because of the income from the Airbnb. Without that train car, we won't have enough funds to afford the mortgage on our home for much longer."

"But it's not just income," Jackson interjected. He cleared his throat, pushing back the wall of emotion that threatened to overcome him. "SAVOUR is a part of us." He closed his eyes, seeing the train car in his mind. "The music box," Jackson said forlornly, mourning the treasures that had been stolen from them along with their beloved SAVOUR. "The perfect set of antlers we found right here." He pointed in front of them at the train tracks. "They were all so..." he searched for the right word but fell silent.

"Special," Marcie finished.

"I know how important antlers are here in the Pacific Northwest, but what makes this music box so significant?" Denise pressed.

"It was full of treasures," Jackson said quietly. "Even the neighbor's kids had left mementos inside."

"Savannah and Darion will be so sad," Marcie said absently.

Jackson shifted on his feet as he considered their disappointment. Savannah's treasure, a small thumb drive full of pictures of the restoration process for SAVOUR, was lost. Both Savannah and Darion had loved being a part of the project. Savannah had used some of those restoration photos in one of her projects before switching majors. Darion's treasures were his pressed flower bookmarks he'd made after foraging with Marcie one summer.

"I'm sure she's backed up the photos," Marcie reassured

Jackson out loud.

Nobody said anything for a long moment before Denise spoke again. "You told me on the phone that you made some improvements to SAVOUR last summer. And the neighbors worked on it with you?"

"It was mostly Savannah. Darion had an internship," Marcie said.

"And you don't suspect the neighbors? Does anyone else in this area have intimate knowledge of your property, the train car, and your schedule?" Denise asked, staring down at her notes while she spoke.

Marcie frowned and Jackson shook his head.

"That carriage weighs so much, it's not like a neighbor would just take it for fun. Whoever took it would need a serious motive," Marcie insisted.

"Are you sure you can't come?" Marcie asked, holding her phone to her ear.

Jackson sat on the couch and stared at the small stack of games on the coffee table.

"They're not coming to game night," she told him after she tapped end.

"Again?" he asked.

She nodded and plopped down beside him.

Their carriage was gone. Their income was gone. The weekly updates from the police had dropped off. Even their friends had abandoned them.

"Did they give a reason this time?"

Marcie just shrugged and shook her head.

"And we're out of white wine," Marcie added.

"Should we call the detective again?" Jackson asked. His last shred of hope clung to the word 'detective' as if such an authority figure could command the return of their lost property.

"I don't think that's going to help," Marcie said.

"I think it's time I got a job again." Jackson admitted defeat and accepted the loss of SAVOUR.

Jackson couldn't muster enough energy to walk out the door. He was leaving behind his retirement. Admitting failure to the FIRE community.

"It's only temporary," Marcie reassured him.

Marcie's phone jingled an alert in seeming response to her words. Neither Jackson nor Marcie moved. The phone jingled its notification again and then again.

"It could be the police?" Jackson said somewhat hopefully.

Marcie grabbed for her phone and stared at the screen; her brows knit together. She held the phone aloft for Jackson to see.

The first alert was for a text link from Nick. Before Jackson had a chance to click the link, more texts filled the screen. Jackson read them aloud for Marcie as they arrived.

"Saw the GoFundMe. So sad to hear the news. Cole."

"Terrible someone took the caboose. I shared with all my friends. John and Lianne."

"What's going on?" Marcie interrupted.

The phone continued to jingle and ping.

"I'm going to click this link and find out," Jackson said as he went back to the first text from Nick.

The page that loaded was indeed a GoFundMe. And front and center was a picture of their caboose. SAVOUR filled the screen. Jackson scrolled down as Marcie leaned over to get a better look. The first paragraph detailed their story about purchasing and restoring the caboose. Several cheery pictures of them in jeans and work gloves alongside Savannah and Darion, were interspersed between the paragraphs. Then a brief explanation of the theft and how Marcie and Jackson relied on the income. Marcie gasped and Jackson read about the purpose of the funds.

"To help find another gem to repurpose. Replacing what is lost."

Jackson's nose burned as he held back the tears. Nick and Sheila had created this campaign to raise money to replace SAVOUR with a new caboose. The largest and initial donation was from Nick and Sheila. They had already reached $1000 in donations, many from their friends and neighbors, but even more from small anonymous donations. Several of the backers suggested names like Gratitude and Hope for the new car.

Marcie's phone continued to ping in Jackson's hand. He refreshed the page. The amount of donations had doubled. The phone rang and Jackson handed it back to Marcie who clicked the call button and held it up to her ear, her eyes wide with shock.

"Hello? Yes, we saw it." Marcie pulled the phone from her ear. "It's Darion," she said to Jackson. "It did? Oh, my goodness! That's great news. We're blown away. Thank you so much, Darion." Marcie pulled the phone from her ear. "He wants to tell you about one of the profiles."

Jackson took the proffered phone.

"Yes?" he asked.

"I went back through the profiles and noticed something about the reviews. Every stay has a review except for one," Darion said.

"He says someone didn't leave us a review," Jackson said for Marcie's sake before putting the phone on speaker.

"Do you remember Jane Goodwin?" Darion asked, his voice loud and clear through the speaker.

"The writer?" Marcie asked.

"Yeah, she didn't actually write you much, but like three of her friends kept messaging you on availability and whatnot?"

"I remember," Jackson said. "She didn't say anything to us directly and only messaged us once asking about the toilet. Her friends purchased the weekend stay for her as a birthday present."

"One of them said she was going to spend the weekend working on a screenplay. A murder mystery," Marcie added.

"Don't you think it's odd she never left a review?" Darion pressed.

"We didn't think anything at the time, no," Jackson frowned and shook his head.

"Well, I didn't see anything else that would make me question any one visitor over another. I've got nothing," Darion sighed.

"Thanks for looking," Jackson said automatically.

"If I think of something else, I'll be sure to let you know.

Sometimes details will pop out when you stop thinking about them directly," Darion added.

"Thanks again, Darion. We really appreciate it and thanks so much for the GoFundMe page. That's a sweet thing for your family to do," Marcie told him.

"Of course. We love SAVOUR almost as much as you do. Talk to you later. Bye."

"Bye," both Marcie and Jackson said.

Marcie's phone jingled again, making her chuckle and switch off the sound. "Now what?" she asked Jackson.

"I guess we look for another car. And thank Nick and Sheila. I guess that's why they were too busy for game night."

"This is the one," Jackson said firmly.

"I knew it as soon as I saw the listing," Marcie said, pride tinging her voice.

"I can't believe it took this long to find one, especially with what seemed the whole state looking."

"The whole world," Marcie added.

"Three months and we've got her."

"She's a beauty. Our Gratitude," Marcie stated.

The caboose would take a lot of work and they would have to transport it up from Oregon, but they had so many helping hands now.

"Should I tell Nick and Sheila?" Marcie asked.

"Let's make sure it's still available first. We can tell them tonight at game night."

"I'm excited to see Darion and Savannah again. It's nice Savannah came home for the summer," Marcie said.

"You want to give the place a call while I make the veggie burgers?" Jackson asked.

Marcie nodded and Jackson handed her the phone.

Hours later the veggie burgers were prepped, and the neighbors knocked on the front door.

"Come on in!" Jackson called from the kitchen.

Several voices filtered through to the kitchen and Jackson finished putting away the last of the dishes he'd used to prep the food.

"Savannah! Darion! So good to see you again. How was school and the new job?" Marcie bustled in from the back of the house.

Savannah dragged her feet and wouldn't meet their eyes. Darion's cheeks were flushed. Nick and Sheila were frowning.

"Is something wrong?" Marcie asked, turning from Nick and Sheila to Jackson.

Jackson shrugged. Nick handed Jackson not one but two bottles of their favorite red wine, and Sheila handed Marcie two bottles of their favorite white wine.

"Chateau Ste Michelle's stock must be going up! What's the occasion?" Jackson joked.

The words hung in the air between them.

Silence.

Nick cleared his throat.

"Savannah has something to tell you," Sheila said.

Savannah stared down at her feet. Jackson was struck by how different she appeared than the last time they'd seen her. Before she'd been boisterous and talkative and open. Now her shoulders crept up to her ears and she hid behind locks of her hair.

"Come, let's sit," Marcie said.

Everyone trooped behind Marcie as she led them to the living room. Jackson set the wine down on the table as he passed.

They sat, Marcie and Jackson in the loveseat, Nick, Sheila, and Darion on the larger sectional couch. Savannah remained standing, one hand grabbing her other arm.

"I'm sorry," she croaked.

"Sorry for what, honey?" Sheila coaxed.

Savannah fished something out of her pocket and held it out toward Jackson. He took it. It was a small thumb drive.

"I took SAVOUR," Savannah finished and plopped into the rocking chair by the couches.

"You... what?" Jackson asked, incredulous. "Is this...?" he trailed off.

Savannah nodded. "I, I didn't take it on purpose. Not really. I don't even remember doing it, but I found this yesterday and Darion said everything was lost. The music box and everything inside. The only way I could have this is if I had taken it. I'm sorry," she finished.

Three months had passed since SAVOUR had mysteriously disappeared. They'd fully funded their GoFundMe through the generous donations of neighbors, friends, and people across the world. They'd finally found the perfect replacement and now... this?

"But where is she now?" Marcie said, looking left and right as if the train car would magically appear in the living room.

Savannah replied with one word before dropping her head into her hands and sobbing.

Lost.

Sheila stood up to comfort Savannah.

Darion spoke, "She didn't mean it. To take the train or to lose it. I pieced together what happened." He looked to Savannah and she nodded.

"You can tell them," she said.

Darion frowned before continuing. "Savannah spent the last month at rehab."

Jackson didn't know what to say.

"But where is it?" Marcie said, clinging to the hope they could recover their beloved caboose.

Darion shrugged again, an apologetic look on his face. "She didn't even remember taking the car until she saw the article last week and found the USB stick yesterday."

Savannah nodded. "But now that I'm here, I remember... I think I might know where the antlers are."

Jackson stood up abruptly. Savannah jumped. "Show us," Jackson said.

They trekked to the empty train tracks in a line. Savannah followed by Marcie, then Jackson, Darion, Nick, and Sheila. Savannah, instead of turning to follow where the twin lines once led, went in the opposite direction.

"The tracks didn't lead that way," Marcie pointed out,

echoing her words to Denise from months before.

On the other side of the tracks a gravel and dirt trail led into the forest and the lesser-traveled patch of land that Jackson and Marcie owned.

Several hundred yards along the trail Jackson bent down to pick up a piece of paper. He unfolded it and revealed the picture of the train car surrounded by the ghost plant Indian-pipe. He gaped at the drawing and handed it wordlessly to Marcie.

"But that's," she faltered. They both stared ahead.

Savannah continued in between the trees, leading them onward across their property.

"I'm not sure how far, but," Savannah began and cut off abruptly.

There, in front of them, was SAVOUR. In the middle of their property. On its side like an abandoned wagon, but there! And Jackson could spot the ends of the antlers, poking up beside the downed caboose.

"Oh, my goodness," Sheila stated the words they were all thinking.

After all these weeks, they'd found it.

"We go live in two minutes!" Nick shouted to the crowd. "And be careful not to step on the ferns!"

Jackson smiled at Marcie and held out his hand. She took it in her own and squeezed. He squeezed lightly back.

SAVOUR, right side up and sitting serenely on its tracks, was now sandwiched between Hope: Hospitality of Peaceful

Elements; and Gratitude: Gifts Revealed at Times Iffy to Uncertain Define Exhilaration. Well, they were still working out the acronyms for the new listings. They had a long line of reservations for the three train cars. Every person who had helped to rebuild and repair the three carriages was invited to stay for a night.

"Are you sure this is what you want?" Savannah asked, looking up at Jackson.

"We forgave you last year, Savannah, and we want everyone to know there are no hard feelings. Besides, SAVOUR is your project too," Jackson smiled at her.

Marcie handed Savannah the set of three petite rectangular blocks of wood. The three train whistles were hand-carved. Each was painted with the words SAVOUR, HOPE, and GRATITUDE.

"Ready?" Nick asked, coming up beside Jackson.

"Let's roll," Jackson said.

Sheila held up her phone, recording the moment the three cars were completed.

Jackson held up the first reclaimed plaque – *Savour the moment.*

He hung it up on top of the door to SAVOUR and the crowd cheered. He nodded to Savannah and she blew the first train whistle to more cheers.

Jackson held up the second piece of wood, the font smaller to accommodate the longer quote, and hung it up on HOPE.

May your choices reflect your hopes, not your fears – Nelson Mandela.

Savannah blew the second whistle. Its melodic tone floated

through the noise of the small gathered crowd of neighbors and friends.

Before hanging the third and final wooden welcome quote, Jackson turned to the crowd and gestured for Marcie to speak.

"Jackson and I want to thank each one of our donors, friends, neighbors, and those who've helped us with this project. It means so much to us that the community has rallied together to see us through the restoration of our beloved little caboose SAVOUR and the addition of two more vintage cars to our small fleet. More than just a source of income, these cars represent our love for history, this town, and its past. SAVOUR, our first caboose was always a symbol of our own love." Marcie smiled affectionately at Jackson.

Jackson took up where she left off. "But we realized that SAVOUR represented more than just our love. It represented our friendship with our neighbors. So, we want to dedicate SAVOUR and HOPE to these two neighbor kids, not children anymore, Savannah and Darion."

"And this final train car, our GRATITUDE, for this town, our neighbors, and all of you watching," Marcie said.

"This car is our way of saying thanks for everything. For believing in us. For helping us. For the support. For everything," Jackson finished.

He held up the final piece of wood so that the crowd could read the writing and Savannah blew on the final whistle.

Joy is the simplest form of gratitude – Karl Barth

Artist's Bio: Stefanie Angelina Allison has been a freelance artist for over thirty years. She's born and raised here in Washington state with a very large loving familia. She attended Yakima Community College for Visual Arts, Art Institute of Seattle for Illustration, and Bellevue College for Graphic Design. Stefanie is currently developing her business, Cherry Awesome Designs, in North Bend with the amazing support system of her husband and two sons.

Author's Bio: Rachel wrote her first autobiography in the fourth grade. She has since written many autobiographical pieces mixed into fiction, as poetry, in her novels, and lately as short stories. She wishes she were taller and that books were made from chocolate. Right now, she's very interested in the FIRE movement and the tiny house lifestyle. During her financial journey over the past year, Rachel discovered that Camp Mustache, a 4-day camp for adults interested in financial independence, was in North Bend. She knew immediately that she had to also use the forested mountains of North Bend as the setting for SAVOUR.

Photo: Tara Sreekumar, plentyopixels.com

DREAM TRAIN ⊗ Minh
Cover Art

Minh
(Minh Ho-Dac Rosen)

Minh's Inspiration: My contribution is my painting of a train in acrylics, very colorful. It came about when I was playing with colors, and all of a sudden, a train emerged. I then went on and further developed my "Dream Train". I love painting people and pets and most of my paintings are of the puppies that came in to the gallery, when the owners were kind enough to let me photograph them.

Artist's Bio: Minh is originally from Vietnam with a background in music and has retired from her long technology teaching career in the New York City public schools. Minh and her husband Larry are now residing in Snoqualmie, with their actor son David living in the Seattle area. Minh still plays the piano and has an art studio in her home. Although her main medium is watercolor, Minh enjoys exploring all mediums. She is a proud member of the Art Gallery of SnoValley, the Mt. Si Artist Guild, and the Northwest Watercolor Society.

Tara Sreekumar
plentyopixels.com
PHOTOGRAPHER - IMAGES OF:

Pepper Allphin's Old Tree
Leslie Kreher's Hideout
Madison Wachter's The Old Tracks
Pepper Allphin's Birdhouse with Train
Cameron Tower & Ellen Rowan's Northbound
International
Minh's Dream Train (cover image)

Sheri J. Kennedy
COVER DESIGNER

AUTHORS & ARTISTS

FVP BOOKS freevalleypublishing.com ⊗ Free-flowing Stories on Facebook

NORTH BEND ART & INDUSTRY North Bend Art and Industry on Facebook

MINH
artgalleryofsnovalley.com/uploads/1/2/3/1/123110905/minh_ros en_bio.pdf

TARA SREEKUMAR plentyopixels.com

JEFFREY COOK clockworkdragon.net ⊗ Twitter @jeffreycook74 ⊗ amazon.com/Jeffrey-Cook/e/B00IRMC3H6 ⊗ freevalleypublishing.com/featured-authors/jeffrey-cook

LESIA TIONGSON PNW Mosaics by Lesia on Facebook

DAVID S. MOORE david-seldon-moore.blog ⊗ freevalleypublishing.com/featured-authors/david-s-moore

LESLIE KREHER LeslieKreherArt.com

CASONDRA BREWSTER casondrabrewster.com ⊗ amazon.com/Casondra-Brewster/e/B00IAFN90U ⊗ freevalleypublishing.com/featured-authors/casondra-brewster

GAYLL MORRISON gayllery.biz

TOMMIA WRIGHT Tommiastablet.blog ⊗ Twitter @ttwright07 ⊗ freevalleypublishing.com/featured-authors/tommia-wright

MADISON WACHTER ashennewt.com ⊗ Ashennewt on Instagram ⊗ Ashennewt by Madison on Facebook

AUTHORS & ARTISTS

VICTORIA BASTEDO Victoria Bastedo author on Facebook ⊗ amazon.com/Victoria-Bastedo/e/B00J1UHDS2 ⊗ freevalleypublishing.com/featured-authors/victoria-bastedo

PEPPER ALLPHIN Art by Pepper on Facebook ⊗ Pepper Allphin on Facebook

KENNEDY J. QUINN misslivadventures.com ⊗ kennedyjquinn on Facebook ⊗ Twitter @kennedyjquinn ⊗ amazon.com/Kennedy-J.-Quinn/e/B01M7TO14L ⊗ freevalleypublishing.com/featured-authors/kennedy-j-quinn

CAMERON TOWER c_tower_studios on Instagram

ELLEN ROWAN Recaptivation on Facebook ⊗ zaellen on Instagram

SHERI J. KENNEDY realitywithatwistbooks.wordpress.com ⊗ sherijkennedyriverside.wordpress.com ⊗.amazon.com/Sheri-J-Kennedy/e/B07FGDBFYQ ⊗ freevalleypublishing.com/featured-authors/sheri-j-kennedy

KRISTIN TETUÁN Art Club PNW on Facebook ⊗ artclubpnw on Instagram

RACHEL BARNARD rachelauthorbarnard.com ⊗ rachelauthorbarnard.com/blog ⊗ rachelbarnardauthor on Facebook ⊗ amazon.com/Rachel-Barnard/e/B00GGBQC9K ⊗ freevalleypublishing.com/featured-authors/rachel-barnard

STEFANIE ALLISON cherryawesomedesigns on Instagram ⊗ etsy.com/shop/cherryawesometumbler

OTHER BOOKS FROM FREEVALLEY PUBLISHING

RACHEL BARNARD At One's Beast ▫ Donuts in an Empty Field ▫ Seize the Donut ▫ Vanessa's Book of Awesome Things ▫ Nichole's Book of Practical Things ▫ Ataxia and the Ravine of Lost Dreams VICTORIA BASTEDO Otterby's Child ▫ Moordym Downs ▫ Roots Entwine ▫ Black Poodle Over Seven Hills ▫ Another Cinderella ▫ The Kiss of the Blue Howler ▫ Mini-Droids and Tea ▫ The Runaway Sleigh Christmas Special ▫ Sunrise Meets the Star ▫ Dear Miklos ▫ Green-Eyed Pursuit ▫ CASONDRA BREWSTER Wilderness Rim ▫ CRISTIE COFFING Carnival Man ▫ JEFFREY COOK Dawn of Steam: First Light ▫ Dawn of Steam: Gods of the Sun ▫ Dawn of Steam: Rising Suns ▫ Foul is Fair ▫ Street Fair ▫ A Fair Fight ▫ All's Fair ▫ Unchosen ▫ Airs & Graces ▫ You're Not a Real Goth SHERI J. KENNEDY Likeness ▫ Feeling Human DAVID S. MOORE The Reverent Athiest ▫ The Martyrs ▫ Restoration ▫ Mind Space KENNEDY J. QUINN The Unwitting Journeys of the Witty Miss Livingstone-Book 1: Journey Key & Book 2: Memory Key & Book 3: Secret Key ▫ Secret Order of the Overworld TOMMIA WRIGHT Reflections on Water

Available on Amazon.com

FVP Books – Where Stories Run Free... FreeValley Publishing connects readers and writers. We aid independent authors in their journey from Story to Publication and in Sharing their Books the way they've always imagined. Stories for all!

FreeValley Publishing was formed in 2013 as a co-op of Snoqualmie Valley & Maple Valley authors based in North Bend, Washington. We are independent authors who work together developing our writing, publishing our works, and sharing marketing events and strategies.

You can find our authors at various festivals and other live events interacting with our readers and community. Check freevalleypublishing.com for the latest news, event schedule and writing tips from our authors and other writers we support.

Our success is sharing our stories with you. Feel free to linger in the Valley and read awhile...

North Bend Art and Industry's becoming the heart of the creative body of North Bend. A central hub, bringing together an eclectic mix of artists & art forms that reflect the character and culture of the Snoqualmie Valley. Where people gather to create, connect, & contribute.

North Bend Art and Industry plans to turn a historic train shed into an "Art Barn" as workshop and learning space for artists in the Valley. The thriving artists will fill the place of 'The Lost Train.'

Made in the USA
Las Vegas, NV
20 September 2021

Praise for What's Up America?

"*What's Up America?* presents the 'why' behind behaviors, values and traditions which many of us may not realize are unique to the U.S., providing us with a base from which to compare our cultures. It is an entertaining book, and a useful resource, not only for newcomers to the U.S., but for those who welcome them."

—*Robin Weber, Manager of Quality and Orientation*
AFS Intercultural Programs USA

"It's a great book. It answers a lot of questions I've had during my first year and a half in the U.S., for instance, why it is so hard to make a true friend with a friendly stranger here, what the American education system looks like, and why Americans like big trucks instead of fuel efficient cars. If you are only going to read one book about Americans, you must read this one."

—*Walt Lee, Chinese director of Futurewei Technologies*

" 'What is America?' Everyone has a different answer to this question, and yet few have thought as deeply or creatively as Diane Asitimbay. She provides a witty and insightful guidebook for understanding that elusive phenomenon, "America," a country born of a democratic idea, inhabited by people from all other nations, and educated by an entertainment industry."

—*Robert A. Pastor, Vice President of International Affairs*
American University

"Diane's clear vision in *What's Up America?* not only makes American culture more understandable to foreigners trying to figure us out, but it's also a wake-up call to we Americans to better understand our own culture. I'd like to see it as a required text in high school civics classes, where it might help students think beyond the local slice of American culture they live in and understand the wonderful diversity of this entire nation, and by doing so, perhaps gain a better understanding of the world as they see how we look to others.

Diane Asitimbay is clearly a powerful and important emerging cultural commentator."

—*Walter Kleine, American editor*

"What other book has illustrations and statistics to show common American attitudes and behavior? This book is truly unique. The author objectively describes the controversial issues affecting Americans, such as multiple identities, non-traditional families, and feelings of patriotism. It is the funniest, clearest, and the truest picture of American culture today."

—*Livia Tommasini, Italian biotech researcher*

What's Up America?
A Foreigner's Guide to Understanding Americans

Diane Asitimbay

Culturelink Press
San Diego, CA

Culturelink Press, P.O. Box 3538, San Diego, CA 92163
Visit our website at: www.culturelinkpress.com

What's Up America?
Copyright © 2005 by Diane Asitimbay

PRINTED IN THE UNITED STATES OF AMERICA

Library of Congress Cataloging-in-Publication Data

Asitimbay, Diane.
     What's Up America? : a foreigner's guide to
understanding Americans / Diane Asitimbay.
        p. cm.
     Includes bibliographical references and index.
     ISBN 0-9759276-0-4

1. United States--Handbooks, manuals, etc. 2. United
States--Social life and customs--1971---Handbooks,
manuals, etc. 3. Visitors, Foreign--United States--
Handbooks, manuals, etc.   I. Title.

E158.A84 2004   973   2004096796

Cover illustration by Jim Whiting
Cover design by Jonathan Gullery
Composition by Ren Daversa

Acknowledgments

I would like to thank my husband Angel and my daughter Sonia for lending their enduring patience and support while writing this book. A special thanks to Gyanam Sadananda, a dear friend who critiqued my book and encouraged me at the same time. I am indebted to Lindy Ferguson for her editing of my early draft and for giving me practical advice. A big thanks to Jennie and Jay Lee, who gave me their feedback throughout this whole project. And finally, to all the international students that have come into my life, for inspiring me to write this book, thank you.

Contents

Introduction

Introduction

Unlike other books that will tell you what American culture is, *What's Up America?* tackles the why questions foreigners ask Americans and no one wants to answer. This book explains the values behind what Americans do. In doing so, it uncovers the hidden rules of the culture and for the first time, reveals the American psyche to foreigners.

Foreigners are often puzzled by Americans. They watch *CNN*, listen to Britney Spears, and buy sweaters at the Gap. Some foreigners may even *feel American* by the way they dress or talk. Yet when they visit or stay in the United States, there are many paradoxes in our culture that are hard to understand.

Street signs, for example, list the many activities Americans cannot do, yet isn't this the land of the free? Or, after international people have watched the life of leisure shown in American films, some of them may be shocked to see American urban streets paved not only with the wealthy eating in gourmet restaurants but also with the homeless sleeping in doorways. How many international visitors are searching for a real live cowboy? Are any of us avoiding New York for fear of getting mugged by all the people stepping out of *The Gangs of New York?*

The influence of American pop culture and media around the world is enormous. Pop culture and images of Americans on TV and film are our largest exports, and they are not even counted in the Gross Domestic Product!

What's Up America? sets out to take the image of Americans out of the television tube and makes them into real live three-dimensional people, with their myths, paradoxes and prejudices. By examining twenty aspects of the American character and lifestyle, it unlocks the secrets of how Americans really live. It will take the international visitor inside the culture to reveal American passions and obsessions up close, where the landscape is often different from what was expected.

While I was writing this book, I realized the risks. We all know Americans come in all shapes and sizes, as do our mindsets and beliefs. Because of our differences, some Americans believe that it is impossible to generalize about American culture without turning to stereotypes. While I realize there are variations on what I have written about American culture, I do believe there are distinguishing cultural patterns that identify American behavior. Though I have made judgments about my culture and people throughout the book, I have often shown the cultural habits of not only the mainstream culture, but also the ethnic subcultures. I have also taken into account some of the regional differences in the United States.

Though *What's Up America?* aims to reduce the culture shock that foreigners face, it is also for Americans who want to broaden their world view. The book compares American cultural habits to other parts of the world. This offers a unique global perspective to American readers. If Americans become more curious about people from other countries and learn something about their cultural habits, it will improve our friendships and business relationships with our global partners.

Since the Internet and cell phone have shrunk the world into a size that everyone is talking about, I believe the international perspective in *What's Up America?* makes this book unlike any other handbook.

These international comparisons are based on my travels and work abroad as a journalist as well as the numerous discussions with international students inside and outside the classroom. The book is also supported by research, ranging from the 2000 U.S. Census reports to current surveys cited at the end of the book. Though the Census is taken every ten years in the United States, I have included government updates whenever they were available. Every effort has been made to make this book as complete and as accurate as possible. Graphs throughout the book illustrate facts and figures about Americans, which I hope readers will find useful.

From candid reflections on the American family, to detailed explanations of the American mindset, this book can be referred to when you have questions about the American landscape and people. It is my hope that these insights into the American character will help those who visit or live in the United States have a more valuable experience. *What's Up America?* can serve as an indispensable tool for Americans who have traveled abroad, plan a trip, or who have contact with international people.

Think of it as a road trip, with every chapter a place to stop and look around at the American landscape. Wherever you are in the journey of your American experience, I would love to hear from you. Please don't hesitate to contact me with your suggestions and comments. You can e-mail me at www.culturelinkpress.com or write me c/o Culturelink Press, P.O. Box 3538, San Diego, CA 92163. Your feedback will contribute valuable information that I will pass on to others through revisions of this book.

Growing Up

16 yrs. old – Getting a driver's license is a rite of passage in the United States.

18 yrs. old – You are an adult by law. You can vote, serve in the military, and marry without your parent's permission.

21 yrs. old – You can drink alcohol.

25-34 yrs. old – You usually live on your own. Only 22% of young Americans, ages 25-34, live at home.

Growing Old

Retirement: 65 yrs. old – About 12.4% or one in every eight Americans is a senior.

75 yrs. or older – Half of women age 75 or older live alone, usually because their spouses have died.

85 yrs. or older – Few seniors live in nursing homes, but after the age of 85, the number of seniors who live in this kind of housing sharply rises to 19%.

Source: National Center for Health Statistics & The U.S. Census Bureau

Chapter 1:

Growing Up & Growing Old

W hen you grow up in the United States, *you*, the individual, are valued more than the family as a whole. Some people call this concept independence; others call it self-centeredness. The notion of individual needs coming before the needs of others is taught before you can even talk. Your mother says, "That's *your* cup, that's *your* spoon, that's *your* chair." The process of mentally stamping objects with your name begins. If a family member or a visitor wants to use whatever is stamped yours, they must ask your permission, even if they are children and you are an adult.

You choose. This is what you hear, like an echo, from every corner of the United States. It begins at an early age. You are faced with several choices throughout the day, that add up to thousands of choices in a lifetime. Parents constantly ask their children what they want. For example, a little boy of around four years old steps into an ice cream shop with his mother. "Andrew," the mom says, "would you like vanilla, chocolate, chocolate chip, caramel, or strawberry?" Before the child understands yet alone remembers his choices, the mom continues, "They have nuts, M&Ms and sprinkles. Would you like a topping on your ice cream or just plain? The kid remains silent and looks confused. The mom, frustrated and impatient, raises her voice at the child: "Andrew, answer me!"

"I want uh . . . Uh . . ." The child tries to decide.

The mom gives up and quickly turns to the clerk to say, "He'll have a vanilla cone with sprinkles on it." This is how the seed of independence is planted in a culture where we are called upon to make up our own minds rather than allow parents to make decisions for us, and this is why some cultures think of us a child-oriented society.

What if a child misbehaves? Americans punish their children by taking away privileges like watching TV or playing video games. Some parents send their misbehaving children to their bedroom. But today, American children have so many entertaining toys and gadgets in their bedroom that this kind of punishment isn't as effective as in the past. At least in the eyes of some people, it isn't considered punishment anymore.

Another form of social isolation is the time-out chair. Children must sit in a chair and be completely silent until parents decide their children have been properly punished according to their misbehavior. How long they must stay in this punishment chair depends on some basic ideas about punishment in America. Children must admit to the parent what they have done wrong, apologize to the parent and promise not to do it again. This is what we call the making-up process.

Grounding, or not being able to go outside with your friends, is another typical punishment. Some parents spank their children when they are young, but after the children get older, parents usually stop. In the United States, schools and courts publicly watch parents closely if parents hit their children. Children are aware of this at an early age because our schools educate them about child abuse. There are even billboards on the roadside advertising a toll-free hotline where children can report their parents for child abuse.

Chores and Allowance

Chores usually begin at about five years old. Young children typically clean their rooms and set or clear away the table. As we get older, we begin to do the dishes, take out the garbage and mow the lawn. Parents view these jobs as necessary for children to learn how to take care of themselves. Some families give money or an allowance to their children for doing chores.

The allowance given to children in the United States, though many parents deny it, is often tied to the work the child does for the parents. If you don't do your chores, you usually don't get an allowance. It is understood that children can spend the money they earned from chores on whatever they want.

Critics believe this practice teaches children to be motivated *only by monetary awards* rather than family responsibility. This attitude of *"What do I get in return?"* is reflected in the dynamics of the family. Many children fail to help family members voluntarily without some concrete, often financial, award being established beforehand. While American parents argue that this practice builds money management skills and the work ethic, it could be argued that children are becoming the newest members of the economy by spending their allowances.

Becoming Independent

American children gradually become used to being physically separated from their parents. It doesn't happen overnight. First, working parents leave their children with babysitters, and at daycare centers where child-care workers take care of them rather than family members. As many families have neighbors without children, parents must make play dates. These are scheduled times when their children play with their friends, and parents often coordinate drop-off and pick-up times with business-like precision.

Then, when a child reaches six or seven years of age, they usually begin to have sleepovers. A child spends the night at a friend's house where they get to watch videos together and eat pizza. Young children are away from their parents at night for the first time. In summer, when school is out, children often go away to day camps like the YMCA or even live at the camps for the entire summer.

By the time American young people reach 16, the age to legally work in this country, they have already spent a great deal of time away from their parents. They have already had experience earning their own money by doing chores at home or neighborhood jobs such as babysitting and mowing the lawn. Teenagers then work part time for "real pay" at a fast-food restaurant. They start to buy their own clothes and CDs and go to the movies with the money they have earned.

There are really two-and-a-half steps to adulthood in the United States: at ages 16, 18 and 21. The first important step happens at 16 years old when you begin to drive. Getting a driver's license in the United States is your passage into adulthood. Your mother no longer has to drop you off and pick you up for your baseball game or dance practice anymore. You can go out alone at night with your friends, and the variety and kinds of activities you can do in your car are endless.

American parents know the dangers and risks of driving and worry, but they allow their children this independence anyway. They weigh the risks against their own needs. Working parents value the teenager who can help them run an errand with the car, from grocery shopping to dropping off film to be developed. The car, and the mobility it provides for the teenager, is the first break with the family, and it is a very personal one.

At this time, parents begin to set curfews as to when the teenager must be home. In many cities across the United States, cities have imposed curfews too. Young people under the age of 18 must be off the streets by 11 p.m. during the week and midnight on weekends. Teens who are going to or from a night job are exempt from the law, as are teens traveling with parents. Curfew laws began as a way to reduce violence, but most young people believe these government rules are unfair.

The second step to adulthood is when you are 18. You become psychologically and legally independent from your parents. You can vote and go into the military, and people can take you to court and sue you instead of your parents. American parents tend to think that now that you are legally and financially responsible for yourself, they can breathe a sigh of relief when you go out with friends. Even if the financial dependence on your parents continues, the psychological and legal independence is clear. Teenagers 18 or older have the attitude of "I can do what I want now that I'm an adult."

Achieving full financial independence from your parents usually occurs after graduating from high school or college. Young people are split into two groups when they graduate from high school: those who look for a full-time job and those who go to college. Whatever path the high school graduate takes, the young person usually lives away from home for the first time.

Knowing this day of final separation will come, parents often remind their children of the future need "to make it on their own." Teenagers already have this in the back of their minds and try to separate themselves emotionally and psychologically from their parents too. From an early age, many smaller steps have been taken to be able to make the final break at 18. Breaking the emotional connection to Mom and Dad is reflected in our language with idiomatic expressions such as "make the break from your parents" or "cut the apron strings."

Parents view severing emotional ties with their children or "letting their children go" as a sign of love. They see it as the ultimate self-sacrifice of suppressing their will and allowing their children to make their own way in life. As their child nears 18 years old, the parents' influence gradually diminishes. Important decisions made by the 18-year-old vary, but might include selecting the college they want to go to, choosing a major or field of study, and leading the kind of lifestyle they want, with friends they desire. The parents' diminished role in their children's life is more or less difficult for many parents to accept.

The last step to full legal independence is at 21, when you are allowed to drink alcohol in the United States. This is a minor step, though, as most teenagers have already tried drinking with their friends or may drink secretly at parties. It is now only a matter of making the fact public and being able to go to bars.

By the age of 21 or 22, many young people want to move to a different city or state from where their parents live. This geographic separation is symbolic of the psychological and emotional distance. While adult children are working or going to college, getting married and having kids, their parents are growing old, so mothers and fathers turn into grandparents who live far from not only their children but also their grandchildren.

Adult children differ on how much contact they maintain with their parents when they live out of state or in a different city. If they live out of state, some adult children call their parents every week, others every month or even only once or twice a year. It is common to "visit the folks," as parents are commonly called, when we take a summer vacation or a major holiday such as Thanksgiving, Christmas, or Easter.

Some families, especially immigrant families who grow up in a subculture, do not follow this pattern of independence. Parents of Mexican Americans or Asian

Americans often play an active role in their adult children's lives beyond 18 years old.

This family separation differs from many countries in the world. In Italy and Southern Europe, young people often live with their parents into their late 20s or 30's, or until they get married. In Arab countries, families have their relatives live in the neighborhood, sometimes within the same block. They frequently live with an extended family. In Japan, because children study all day, maintaining a close relationship to their dads is particularly difficult. Japanese fathers often are away from their homes more hours than their American counterparts. They frequently dine with colleagues after work besides the long hours spent working at their jobs. Some Japanese dads might even work in another city, and visit their families on weekends. Yet when it comes time to marrying and establishing households, Japanese married couples usually live close to their families. In Korea, it is still common for a married couple to live with the husband's parents and to take care of them as they age.

Growing Old

While their children are growing up, parents are growing old. Then they turn 65, retire, and become senior citizens. Now they have a lot of free time on their hands. In the United States, seniors play golf and bingo, take classes, gamble and travel to other countries. Generally, they fill their free time with many activities they were unable to pursue when working.

American seniors cherish this "individual pursuit of happiness." As parents, they are eager to let their children leave home at 18. For twenty years, they haven't had any children living with them. When grandchildren finally come along, some active seniors choose not to take care of them. That responsibility would hinder them from pursuing their self-fulfilling activities. Others would rather not be around the noise and activity that young children bring.

The paradox of this self-centered lifestyle is that many of these same seniors volunteer many hours at museums, churches, historical societies, and other civic organizations. They even volunteer at youth organizations and schools where they take care of children many hours a week. Yet many seniors who are grandparents may spend little time with their own grandchildren.

Life may turn upside down, though, for both the adult children and the aging parent, in a single moment if a senior parent has a heart attack or is diagnosed with a serious medical condition.

The whole issue of independence that was settled once and for all after high school or college comes back again. But this time, the process is reversed. Parents are struggling to maintain their independence from their adult children.

But for many families, the circle has been broken. Over the course of twenty to thirty years, day-to-day life for both the parents and the adult children has become a mystery. Emotional distance has been established in the years of long-distance, routine phone calls. Adult children may look at the sickly parent as an inconvenience rather than feel the passionate need to take care of them.

The reality is that many adult children do not want their parents to live with them. Many adult children are not ready to make sacrifices for their aging parents. These sacrifices may include taking time off from their jobs, or reducing their hours if both husband and wife hold down jobs. In short, they are not willing to change their lifestyle in that way.

On the other hand, older people try not to depend on their adult children. They feel guilty for needing their children. Our culture admires the strong and teaches us not to show our weak side. If you ask senior citizens why they don't live with their children, you will most likely hear, "I don't want to be a burden to my children."

What does being a burden mean to them? If you press a senior into answering, it usually revolves around being forced to ask their adult children to do simple errands for them.

Being able to drive yourself where you want to go when you're old is very important. Driving is symbolic of independence in American culture. Remember when you were 16 years old and this was the rite of passage? Seniors also cherish their driver's license and are reluctant to give it up no matter how bad their eyesight is or how much medication they are taking. They feel it is a sign of defeat in the battle to stay independent.

The pressure of not living with your parents after 18 is just as strong as not living with your children when you are 80.

That's why there are many kinds of living arrangements for seniors. There are senior complexes, assisted living complexes, basic nursing homes, skilled nursing homes, and a myriad of other kinds of housing for seniors today. Many foreigners mistakenly believe most Americans put their parents in nursing homes. Actually, only 4% of seniors 65 to 85 years of age live in nursing homes in the United States according to the National Center for Health Statistics. Most seniors live alone or with their husband or wife. For seniors over 85 years old, however, the numbers dramatically increase to 19%. By this age, many seniors have become widowed and have more serious medical conditions.

A few seniors realize that no one will take care of them if they get sick and live far from their children. They get frightened at the thought of being sick and alone before any major medical problems occur. Some seniors might even get frightened enough to sell their home and move close to where their children are.

It is a myth that the American government takes the place of the family institution and financially supports the elderly in the United States. When you turn 65 and retire, you get two things to help you live on a very reduced income. You get free medical insurance called Medicare, which many doctors do not accept, as they are only minimally reimbursed. And you may get a pension or a social security check.

Not everyone gets social security in the United States when they turn 65, either. Only people who have worked a certain number of years, which amounts to about 10 years of full-time work, receive a regular check. Or when your spouse dies, you may collect a major portion of his or her social security check.

The average senior income from social security is $14,000 a year. This is next to impossible to live on unless you have no house payment. This is why seniors have so many discounts in our society, ranging from reduced prices on entertainment, senior days in stores, and a special rate for bus passes.

Prescription drugs are extremely expensive in the United States, and many of these drugs are not covered by this government insurance. This forces seniors to buy their medicines in cheaper places like Canada and Mexico.

Who will take care of us when we are old? *Nobody* has been the answer so far in our culture. Seniors make up 12% of American society today, and this age group is the fastest growing segment of our population. As we live longer and have fewer children, the need for adult children to take care of their aging parents will become greater. Will it be great enough to change our youth-centered culture?

Notes

"In America, the young are always ready to give those who are older than themselves the full benefits of their inexperience."

– Oscar Wilde, humorist (1856-1900)

Don't Worry, Be Happy.

The yellow smiley face is a universal symbol of good cheer. This cultural icon was created by Harvey Ball in 1963 as part of a campaign to improve employee morale at an insurance company.

Have a Nice Day! is one of the most overused expressions in the United States. Since the 1970's, it has been used to end a conversation in place of the traditional "goodbye."

Does this goodbye phrase truly cheer someone up or does it force people to hide how they really feel? Customer service people are often expected to use this phrase to show enthusiasm to customers.

Sweden or Switzerland?

○ Americans age 18 to 24 came in next to last among nine countries in the National Geographic and Roper 2002 Survey, a survey which measured students' knowledge of geography.

○ On this geographic survey, more than half, 56%, of Americans could not locate India, home to 17% of the world's population.

Chapter 2:

Thinking American

W hy are Americans always smiling? We are walking "smiley signs" ending our conversations with, "Have a nice day." Those happy words seem to slip from our tongues without any real thought. "Don't worry, be happy." There are smiley face stickers and icons, and there is even a huge smiley face structure off Interstate 80, "Smiley, the Friendly Greeter," a city landmark for a small town in Illinois.

Customer service in stores is built on a grin. At the checkout counter, cashiers greet you with a rehearsed happy face and ask, "Was everything okay?" or "Did you find everything you needed?"

What enormous pressure we have in this culture to at least *look* happy. If you appear too serious, people will chide you by saying, "Don't look so serious." Or they might ask you, "Is something wrong?" It's common to hear, "Yes, I'm having a bad day." Then the person typically replies, "Oh, I'm sorry to hear that," or "That's too bad." This is a ritual that usually doesn't go further than a polite exchange of unhappiness and sympathy.

This need to be eternally pleasant seems to be a contradiction in the United States, where the freedom to speak up and say what you feel is honestly valued. Public discourse in the form of debates before a presidential campaign is common. You can protest in front of a business or government organization, expressing your personal opinion in a public place. Yet at the same time, there is an unwritten cultural rule that many Americans learn from an early age. Parents usually teach their children to be polite and not offend anyone. If the topic is negative or if children want to criticize someone, they should keep their opinions to themselves. We are taught to talk only about pleasant subjects. This is why we may appear so superficial and, when taken to the extreme, not honest about the way we feel towards someone. We aren't supposed to talk about religion, politics, and sex because it might make other people feel uncomfortable.

We have happy hours at bars and restaurants, when cheaper drinks are offered so you can drink more and be happier. McDonald's sells us not a children's hamburger but a "Happy Meal." Your bank and dentist send you cards wishing you a happy birthday.

Happiness is commercialized and packaged to be bought and sold. The deep realities of human existence, such as sickness, old age and death, are not discussed. We avoid coming face to face with these aspects of life, yet we expect to have a rich, emotional connection to people.

We sell happiness in a bottle. Do you know how many American men and women are on Prozac or other forms of anti-depressants? It is estimated that between 20-25 million Americans are taking anti-depressants to feel good.

Our movies usually end happily. They send out a distorted vision of real life in our society but reveal how Americans want their lives to be. *Pretty Woman* and *Maid in Manhattan* are Cinderella stories of today. Children are first raised on fairy tales where the prince finds the slipper of his princess and lives happily ever after. The poor girl marries the rich man and lives in bliss. Or in action movies, the hero is shot at numerous times, surviving bullets and car crashes, but he never dies. Adult fairy tales are very popular in movies because we search for that version of happiness.

Happiness is featured in television sitcoms like *Jerry Seinfeld* and *Friends*, which usually create one-liner jokes every few seconds and expect you to laugh with the prerecorded laughter. The one-liner is the classic American brand of humor. It is basically a put down or an insult said in a joking way, so that you laugh at yourself rather than feel offended or hurt.

Whether we like you or not, the American style of conversing is mainly through jokes. Most Americans have a very direct sense of humor compared to the sophisticated British wit. Ethnic jokes were commonly told in the past but today, jokes are mostly told about gender, weakness of character, and we have plenty of lawyer jokes too.

Many Americans are thought to be gullible. We readily trust in people's words without analyzing or judging the source. "You have my word," we say. By looking at people in the eye, we judge whether they are telling the truth or not.

Geographically Illiterate

Many Americans are geographically illiterate. We don't know Switzerland from Sweden. We're not sure if people in Brazil speak Spanish or Portuguese. In a recent geography poll, more than 3,000 young people (18-24 year olds) were surveyed in nine countries about their knowledge of geography. Overall, Sweden scored the highest and the United States was next to last. About 11 percent of young Americans couldn't even locate the United States on an unlabeled world map, 29 percent couldn't locate the Pacific Ocean, 58 percent didn't know where France was, and 69 percent couldn't find the United Kingdom.

The paradox of living in a country that is a leader in global politics, yet has the majority of people ignorant about the rest of the world, is a fact of American culture. Young people know more about the South Pacific island featured on the TV show *Survivor* than where Iraq and Israel are.

Geography is usually not required in American schools and is instead, offered as an elective. Students may avoid taking a class because it's not a subject on our standardized tests. Schools focus on preparing students in core subjects that they will later be tested on: mathematics, science, and English. In elementary school, Americans study their native state for one whole school year by learning the state's flower, resources, motto, and history as part of the subject of social science. Then we briefly study geography again in high school in our American History and World History classes, whose main focus is a history of wars and heroes. It is puzzling to think that students could learn history without basic geography skills.

Only 20% of Americans have traveled or studied abroad in any given year. Although traveling to another country surely would help shed some of the geographic ignorance, most Americans grow up visiting sites within the United States. It is common to go to other states to visit relatives or to go camping in national parks. Families often drive to these places, and see their vacation as a chance to get away from the city.

Taking the whole family to another country for vacation is quite unusual as well as expensive. The American concept for vacation is often anti-urban as well. Going to the countryside or beach to absorb the natural environment and get away from traffic is often sought rather than seeing a large city in another country and exploring its cultural wealth.

Another explanation for our ignorance of other countries is that the vast majority of Americans, about 85%, speak only one language. When Americans do travel abroad, they don't want to learn another language. Many are not forced to, as English is widely spoken in many of the European countries that Americans like to visit. Though American students are increasingly going to other countries such as Spain and Italy, the United Kingdom is by far the leading destination for American students, according to a 2003 Open Doors report, an annual report that tracks college students who study overseas.

Still another part of our geographical illiteracy can be explained by our history. Early American colonists came here and settled down on unchartered territory. We were never forced to defend our land from foreign conquerors. To the east and the west, the United States has no border countries to contend with. The Pacific and the Atlantic oceans have protected and isolated us from other continents. This geographical inheritance has produced an American mindset that views foreigners as a labor force, and not as a cultural or language force.

Number Crazy

How much and how many are always on our minds. We rate every human experience and dissect it into numbers.

Listen to our traffic reports. We report on traffic as if it were a science with codes for highways and congestion: "Four lanes open on the eastbound 8 and a 25-minute wait off the 15-interchange where it merges with the 805, you have a 3-car pileup averaging a 45-minute delay on the 5. Stay tuned for updates every 15 minutes."

Weather reports are similar with sunshine measured by UV (ultraviolet) indexes and humidity and precipitation percentages. All this number jargon makes our head spin, when in reality, all we want to know is the temperature and whether it's going to rain or not.

Americans suffer from a disease that I call *"the -est"* problem. We are a nation of superlatives. Statistics published in newspapers or seen on TV often are selected to show the United States as the best in everything and the only important country.

You can really see *"the -est"* problem in our media. We publish lists of "the best" all the time. We quantify everything and then compare it to other countries and people. The fastest growing religion is Islam, the richest American is Bill Gates and the biggest hit in the movie theaters was *The Titanic. The New York Times* produces a bestseller list of books that is printed weekly in our newspapers. And of course, we love the ultimate *-est* book, the *Guinness Book of World Records*. Nothing in the United States can be just pleasant, good or fair. It must be super, fantastic, wonderful or awesome, the prettiest, the fastest, the highest and the best. If you talk about averages or the median, Americans will ask you for the minimum and maximum or the best and the worst. We are a nation of extremes. We think moderation is boring.

International news practically doesn't exist in the United States. Even *The New York Times*, one of the most respected newspapers in the country, devotes only a few pages to international news. Of course, if you have cable, there is always *CNN* and there is *BBC*, but many times the focus is just on crises and conflicts in political parts of the world that the United States is militarily involved in. When the World Cup was held in the United States in 1994, Americans who had no cable TV service had to watch the games in Spanish because the major network channels only televised games when the Americans played. We were hosting the World Cup and we only wanted to see our country's team play? This was more than just the lack of interest in soccer in the United States. It demonstrated that only "American" sports are considered important enough for prime time television.

A Television Mind

When I ask international students whom they admire most in their lives, they usually say their parents or grandparents. When I ask the same question to American students, most name a famous movie or TV star.

American parents spend an average of 38.5 minutes having meaningful conversation with their children per week, according to the American Family Research Council. Yet the American child spends 19 hours and 40 minutes watching television per week, reports Nielsen, a television ratings service. It wouldn't be surprising if American children recognized more television characters than real famous people. Or that TV exercises a greater influence on American children than their parents do.

The American mind is a TV mind. The average American has the TV on for 7 hours and 40 minutes a day and watches over 4 hours of programs a day.

Besides the fact that the TV set is turned on several hours a day at home, the television screen is also turned on in public places. The TV is seen in health clubs, bars and restaurants and in doctors' and mechanics' waiting rooms. Even when we go to a baseball game where we are paying to see the action and players in person, people watch an enormous screen. Viewing is preferred to doing. The constant noise from the TV in public places offers very little silence for people to read and think. It may confirm the idea that Americans are not comfortable in silence.

In our homes too, many American parties are planned around watching television. You are invited to come to our house and watch the Super Bowl, the Rose Bowl, the Oscars, the Macy's Thanksgiving Parade, and the Times Square ball dropping on New Year's Eve. You sit in front of the television with other guests and exchange commentary about what you watch. Some people invite guests to their home and have the TV turned on in the background just in case they don't find enough to talk about.

Many Americans talk about TV programs as if the knowledge and adventures on TV were their own. Sharing first-hand experience is becoming rare, and TV programs often replace genuine topics of conversation. Seeing the world through a commercial box comes with a price, though. Commercials are constantly interrupting our programs asking us to buy this product or that, so our attention spans are split into tiny parts too.

Talking as a Game

Be prepared to play ping-pong when you talk to Americans. You say something brief, usually no more than one sentence. Then the other person asks a question. The other person answers it and says something short again. Your head bobs back and forth as you watch two Americans talk to each other.

Many aspects of our culture use sports and games as a metaphor. We use the notion of a ball in our daily speech and particularly in business. It's your turn to decide or act can be *the ball is in your court*. When you avoid responsibility *you drop the ball*. You *pitch an idea* means presenting a person with your idea, with the intention of convincing them of your plan. Have you done your job thoroughly? Then you've *covered all the bases*. You're a *big hitter, a major player*, meaning an important competitor in business.

We borrow words from many sports, but baseball, in particular is widely used. We present an idea or *throw out* an idea. We give you two chances in the *game of life* or business. With the third chance, you lose or face the consequences. It's *three strikes and you're out*.

We can also think of dating as a game, with baseball capturing the hearts of Americans. In a chauvinistic way, Americans males often use slang to express how far they physically advance with a woman on a date. When a male says he only got to *first base* this means he was only able to hold hands with the girl or give her a peck on the cheek.

Getting to *second base* might mean he managed to kiss her, *third base* he made out with her or was able to touch her. Finally, if he *hit a home run*, he managed to sleep with her. He *scored*! If he *struck out*, this means he was unsuccessful at advancing to any of these bases with the girl.

Lonely or Alone?

We often feel isolated and alone in the United States. One in every four Americans lives alone. We tell the most personal details of our lives to strangers in grocery lines, in restaurants, and to therapists, but not to people we know or family members. When Americans have a serious problem in a relationship, we run to the therapist. The pressure in our society to be self-reliant is so strong that we don't want to expose our weaknesses and be judged by our friends and family. We choose the stranger in seeking help to solve our problems. We also trust in their specialized knowledge more than our own family.

Dogmatic

Why are Americans so dogmatic? Americans like a yes or no when asked a question. We dislike ambiguity. We see reality in black and white photos rather than in color. Things that can't be researched to find facts and conclusions make us feel uneasy. Americans think in a linear, straight ahead method and don't like digressions.

When Americans fail to understand each other, we might say, "I don't understand your line of reasoning," or if we speak indirectly about a topic, we might urge the other person to "please get to the point." Americans often dislike uncertainty. When we ask you what you want to do or where you want to go, we usually feel frustrated with any hesitation or lengthy explanation. We might even ask you rather abruptly, *"Yes or No?"* to get to the final clear-cut answer. It's better to be sure and wrong than not to know. Americans tend not to wait for someone to make decisions that might entail many factors to consider. We think taking action and making mistakes helps us learn, so waiting until you are absolutely certain is considered a waste of time.

This is unlike Asian cultures and more collective cultures, where a consultation with a group is necessary in order to reach a decision. Getting other people's opinions, discussing the pros and cons of the decision, reaching a consensus from colleagues and then making a kind of collective decision often takes more time. The ultimate decision itself may be a conditional yes or no, and not a simple yes and no that many Americans seek.

Notes

"Americans seem sometimes to believe that if you are a thinker you must be a frowning bore, because thinking is so damn serious."

– Jacques Maritain, French philosopher (1882-1973)

Pride & Prejudice in the U.S.

Inside their own communities, Americans still give nicknames to various groups in our society based on skin color.

Apples – Native Americans who act white and follow a non-Indian lifestyle often get the nickname "apples," red on the outside, white on the inside.

Bananas or **Twinkies** – Asians born in the United States who have adopted the mainstream values and customs are frequently called "bananas" or "twinkies," yellow on the outside, white on the inside.

Oreos – African Americans who act white on the inside, and black on the outside are sometimes called "oreos."

Güero or **Blanco** *(terms for light skin)* & **Moreno** or **Negro** *(terms for dark skin)* – Spanish speakers often use these nicknames for people inside and outside their community.

Hate Crimes in the United States

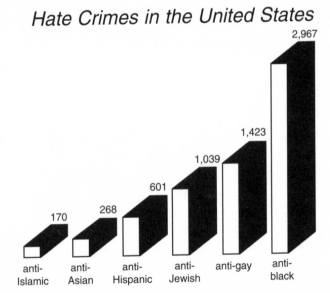

anti-Islamic	anti-Asian	anti-Hispanic	anti-Jewish	anti-gay	anti-black
170	268	601	1,039	1,423	2,967

Source: Federal Bureau of Investigation, Uniform Crime Reports, 2002

Chapter 3:

Under Our Skin

I s there such a thing as a pure or true American? Do you mean the Native Americans who were living here before the Europeans discovered them? Today, Indians or Native Americans number less than 1% of the population. Over the course of four hundred years of European contact, those who survived have married people outside their tribe and race. An Indian from a tribe with a low intermarriage rate would be the closest thing to a pure or true American as you could get today.

Christopher Columbus was lost when he landed in America in 1492. He thought he was in India. That's why he called the natives here "Indians." Most of us celebrate the founding of America in a civic holiday called Columbus Day, but for the Indians, it is a Day of Mourning. It marks the beginning of European contact, which brought diseases that killed 90% of their people.

The Native American struggle continues today, long after the Indian Wars officially ended in 1890. Half of the

Home Away from Home

Vietnamese: "Little Saigon" Chicago, Illinois

Arabs: Dearborn, Michigan

Swiss: New Glarus, Wisconsin

Mexicans: Olivera Street, Los Angeles

Greeks: Greektown, Detroit, Michigan

Portuguese: New Bedford, Massachusetts

Koreans: Koreatown, Los Angeles

Cubans: Little Havana, Miami, Florida

Chinese: Chinatown, San Francisco & NY City

Italians: Little Italy, Baltimore, Maryland

Japanese: Japantown, San Francisco, California

Germans: Cincinnati, Ohio

The foreign born make up 12% of the U.S. population. Ethnic neighborhoods are found all across the country as a result of many immigrant groups moving to the U.S. These immigrant communities offer ethnic markets and restaurants. Many of these enclaves also have newspapers and social networking groups.

Native Americans are assimilated into urban areas, the 1994 U.S. Census reports, while nearly half of Native Americans still live on reservations.

Some tribes are still fighting to get their land back. Many tribes are suing the U.S. government over land promised to them more than a hundred years ago. Some Indian reservations have set up casinos in the past decade, and are doing financially better than other Indians living on reservations that have no gambling. Reservation Indians are some of the poorest Americans in the country. They have little income and depend on federal government food and money to survive.

Native Americans are also fighting the practice of using tribal names and images for college and professional sports teams. These images reinforce the Indian as a warrior when in reality, most members of the hundreds of Indian tribes were artisans, weavers, pottery makers, and fishermen, among other non-warrior occupations.

It is interesting to note that in the United States the first white colonists tried to capture the Indians and make them into a cheap labor force, but research shows that most Indians got sick and died from the diseases that Europeans brought. Other Indians escaped and hid in the forests and vast land they knew better than the Europeans. If the colonists had been successful in capturing and enslaving them, the United States might have a very different population today. It might have looked similar to the Latin America of today, with a large majority of mestizos and indigenous languages actively spoken.

But it didn't happen that way. Largely unsuccessful with the Indians, the European colonists looked to importing slaves from West Africa as a source of cheap labor in order to sell their sugar and tobacco to international markets.

As soon as the slave trade began in this country, interracial marriage was banned. Puritan colonists from the Protestant Church wanted to keep their people pure of other races. In Brazil and Spanish America, however, the

Roman Catholic Church was the dominant institution and allowed more mixing of the races. So today, race isn't as much of an issue in Brazil and Latin American countries as it is in the United States.

African Americans are the only immigrants that were forced to come here, arriving chained to a ship. They were inspected and bought like property. The master stripped them of their West African names, gave them any first name they wanted, and didn't even bother to give them a last name.

Many African Americans were not permitted to have families. Husbands, wives, and children were sold to different slave masters. Some slave masters would rape African women, and after the African slave gave birth to the child, they could be kept with the master's family or be bought and sold. It is from this history that African Americans face an enormous task if they want to trace their history; some learn that it often stops at a slave ship.

How do we identify ourselves in such a mixed culture? The paradox consists of having a mental map with landmarks of Indian removal and black slavery, yet history books are filled with success stories of immigration and assimilation. While European Americans may tell you a story of assimilation, for Native and African Americans, there are other stories to be told of removal and separation.

Many foreigners believe in the myth that the United States is a melting pot or a mix of races blended together to make one nation, a myth which ignores our long history of trying to keep races apart.

What melting pot? If our nation poses for a class picture, other people might see faces of every color, but to the American eye, it would be developed in black and white.

We still have segregation. Though segregation is illegal, we still have inner-city schools made up largely of blacks, Hispanics, and other minorities, while suburban schools are mainly white. We have neighborhoods where an African

American family moves in and the whites move out.

The American government has always divided its people by race. When the U.S. Census began counting people in 1790, it divided people into free white men and women and slaves.

Today, the United States divides its 290 million people into five major categories of White, African American, Hispanic, Asian, and Native American. In the 2000 Census, the government let us choose more than one category of race. This national census had 63 racial categories to check your mixed blood compared to the traditional five. For the first time in history, the U.S. government recognizes mixed blood in this country.

Racial categories, however, make no sense even with more choices. White and black are based on skin color. We are not white and black. These are arbitrary identifiers. Whites are all various shades of skin colors, yellowish brown, pinkish white, copper brown, olive-skinned, and many of us are closer to brown although we don't call ourselves Brown.

The currently used term of African American is based on a continent where blacks were forced to leave. Hispanic is a collective term based on language, or whether the person speaks Spanish. The Asian category refers to all Taiwanese, Chinese, Japanese, Korean, Indians from India, and any other nationality that comes from the continent of Asia.

The U.S. government identifies us one way, but we have chosen to identify ourselves in our own ways.

Although the federal government puts everyone together into an umbrella term, Hispanic, Mexican Americans don't think of themselves as Hispanic. They are Latinos or Chicanos. They often ask each other what city their relatives were originally from in Mexico. Are you a Poblano, Oaxacan, or Chilango from Mexico City? These regional origins are reflected in the music and the food of the Mexican communities living in metropolitan areas throughout the United States.

The true number of Hispanics is hard to measure. The term Hispanic is considered an ethnic group by the federal government, and not a race. Hispanics can be of any race, black or white.

Other nationalities falling into the Hispanic category identify themselves from their respective nation of origin. So you have Puerto Ricans, Cubans, and Salvadorans, all retaining their native country's identity and food customs.

Asian Americans call themselves Asians and ask each other which generation they are from, giving each other a reference point as to how long they have been in the United States. It is a marker for assimilation as well. Are you first generation, second generation or third generation? The language of Taiwanese, Cantonese, and Japanese is usually understood by the first generation but not always spoken very well. By the second generation, it is understood and spoken less, and by the third generation it is often lost entirely.

Asians adapt to the mainstream culture rather quickly and this is reflected in the affectionate nickname Asian Americans call themselves, "bananas" They are yellow on the outside and white in the middle. Asians born in the United States but originally from India often call themselves an *"ABCD,"* which stands for an "American Born Confused Desi." *Desiz*, "desh" is the Hindi word for country and "desi" is countrymen. This term refers to Indians born in the United States who are trying to balance their traditional Indian roots with modern American ways. This struggle for cultural identity can be seen in the recent movies *American Desi* and *Bend It Like Beckham*. *Desiz* distinguish themselves from those who have recently arrived from India.

Asians also identify with other Asians by the values they share, with education being one of the most important values. It is common for Asian parents to pay for their children's college education including graduate school. This financial support throughout their childhood and college sets this minority group apart from other groups, including whites. This investment in their children is seen as a circle. Parents will take care of their children and in turn, adult children will someday take care of their elderly parents. This respect for the parents often strongly connects the Asian community.

African Americans feel a natural affinity to other blacks through their history of not being treated equally. How blacks speak often identifies how well they have adapted to the mainstream white majority. Blacks have an insider language with their black brothers and sisters. They are often bilingual, able to use standard English in schools but talk the slang with their black friends and family at home.

Unfortunately, many foreigners are afraid of blacks when they come to the United States because they have never personally known a black person. Or they are prejudiced against them because television images of gangs and street life reinforce negative stereotypes.

Native Americans identify themselves by tribe as Cherokees, Sioux, Chippewas, Iroquois, Apaches, and Navahos. There are more than 700 tribes in the United States, though the federal government only recognizes about 542 of them. Each tribe has a certain blood requirement; for example, 1/4 Indian can usually qualify you for a certain tribe.

The number of Indians has actually increased over the last decade as some tribes fight over how they will distribute the gambling revenue from the numerous casinos set up on Indian reservations. For example, the Cherokees don't need any proof of their ancestry as it is strictly based on self-identification. This tribe now registers as the largest Indian tribe in the United States.

When you ask European Americans where they are from, they speak in percentages too. They are 1/4 German, 1/4 Irish and the other half English. If you probe deeper and ask them what city in Europe, they usually do not know. Great, great grandmother left behind all her relatives in the old country. Family surnames were often shortened or misspelled by the Immigration Officer when relatives stepped off the boat. Their mother tongue suddenly became a private language of the past, to be only spoken at home, and given up in one or two generations. It is this history, this mental map, that European Americans have of their ancestry. No elaborate family trees, only a sketchy story retold to those who ask. A family history that is usually passed down orally from one generation to the next by an older relative.

Whites don't use the term European American because they make up the majority of people in the United States. They feel no need to be identified by the continent of origin. Since European Americans are the only group in the United States to have a history of assimilation rather than discrimination, their history is the one written down in our history books and taught in our schools.

All this ethnic diversity in the United States surprises foreigners, especially the Koreans and Japanese. These nuances and distinctions of racial identity in the United States do not exist in highly homogenous cultures. Ancestors have an important role in Confucianism and many Koreans and Japanese have a huge family book that traces their ancestry back many generations. They have elaborate ceremonies remembering their ancestors on the day they died, with special food and religious rites. Names have special significance and help trace your ancestry, too.

Some Americans have regular family reunions that are centered around a holiday or an annual picnic. A family tree may even be created by a relative that has researched the family history. Still, talking about our ancestors is not very common in the United States. Our future plans are much more popular topics for conversation. Now you know why Americans prefer to look to the future because we know little about our past.

Notes

"I look to a day when people will not be judged by the color of their skin, but by the content of their character."

– Martin Luther King, Jr., civil rights leader (1929-1968)

American Families

The typical American family is no longer the husband, wife and two children. Families come in all shapes and sizes in the U.S.

People who live alone may have been married, widowed, divorced or may eventually marry. Single parents may be single by choice or may have been counted as married before.

Gay couples can be counted as individuals living alone or unmarried couples living together.

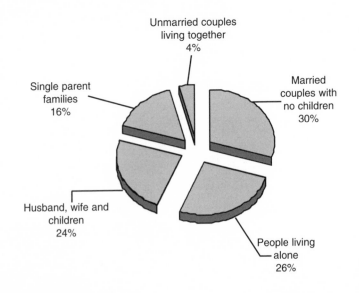

Unmarried couples living together
4%

Married couples with no children
30%

Single parent families
16%

Husband, wife and children
24%

People living alone
26%

Source: 2000 U.S. Census

Chapter 4:

Family Ties & Knots

W hat is the American family? It's the single mother with children, the grandmother who is raising the grandchild, the couple who chooses not to have children, the unmarried couple living together, and the lesbian or gay couple who adopt a child. Many American families do not fit the stereotype of a traditional family with the husband, wife, and children. Even when we have married couples with children, we might have husbands who stay home while their wives support the family.

No wonder most of us feel uncomfortable when asked about our families when we first meet people. These questions are considered very personal because we have mixed feelings. How will we be judged by those who have traditional views of a family? We feel defensive about the family question. It's not easy to explain the complicated patterns of American families when we do not know the expectations of the other person.

Some state governments are slowly recognizing some

of these new arrangements of families. Currently, there are a handful of states that favor same-sex couples. The state of Vermont has a civil union law, and California, Hawaii and New Jersey have domestic partnership laws that give same-sex couples the rights of traditional marriages. These laws follow the trend of nations such as Germany, France, Sweden, Denmark, and Canada, which recognize new forms of partnerships. Some private employers use the new terms *significant other, partner* or *companion* in redefining their policies regarding health insurance. In the United States, Massachusetts has become the first state to legally marry gay couples.

By the time American women marry and decide to have children, many have been on birth control for many years. If they have waited until their late 30's or 40's, some women may face problems having children. They undergo expensive fertility injections, and some couples are successful in having children with this treatment.

Other couples give up trying to have children naturally and decide to adopt. Since Americans have very few children today, it is much harder to adopt American children. While other countries can provide American families with infants, the average age of a child in a foster home is 8 years old in the United States, according to the National Council for Adoption.

Adopting from a foreign country usually takes about a year and adopting an infant from a foster home in the United States can take several years. That is why Americans adopt foreign children. Some American parents also choose to adopt from overseas to avoid a possible fight with the birth parents to reclaim custody of the adopted child later in life. South Korea is the top foreign source for adopted children in the United States. Many children also come from China, Russia and Mexico. Girls are adopted (835,000) more often than boys (750,000). Foreign adoptions make up 13% of the total American adoptions.

In South Korea, there are more baby girls than boys in

orphanages, since many families prefer a first-born son to take care of them when they are older.

Single women are adopting children in growing numbers too, as it is becoming more socially acceptable to be a single mother. The current Census figures show that adopted children make up about 2.5% of America's 65 million children. Many of those children are adopted by their relatives or their stepmother or father.

Three million children are being raised by gay and lesbian parents in the United States, estimates a gay rights organization, The Family Pride Coalition. All but three states allow unmarried people to adopt the children. The culture is deeply divided on gay marriages and gay parenting. The future will show how willing Americans are to accept children with two moms or two dads.

Another kind of family that is on the increase is the American childless couple, where the woman is physically able to have children but chooses not to. Many childless couples want to maintain their flexible lifestyles. Some may want to travel or dedicate themselves entirely to their careers and don't want the commitment involved with raising children.

Tying the Knot

How easy is it to be married if you are heterosexual? Very easy. In Las Vegas, Nevada, 24-hour chapels will marry you without a waiting period. Weddings are the second largest industry in Nevada after gambling. You can get married in a helicopter, a hot air balloon, or by a clerk dressed up as Elvis Presley.

When you come back for the ceremony, you need at least one witness to be present. Some City Halls even provide the witness. The marriage ceremony lasts about ten minutes. The total cost to get married in this civil way is $50-$100 for the marriage license and ceremony.

Once married, the inequality of the sexes in the United

States emerges. Despite the idea of equality in our heads, in practice, most American men and women are not even close to being equal when it comes to caring for their children and doing housework. Polls have shown that American women today still do most of the housework and cooking just like generations ago. The mother typically disciplines during the day while threatening to tell the father later. If the mother tells the father what happened during the day, the child might get another scolding from the father when he gets home.

Untying the Knot

The fear of divorce keeps many American young adults from getting married. They don't want to be just another divorce statistic. It is well known than almost half of our marriages end up in divorce. It is a bit ironic that when we get married, we worry about getting divorced first, and that when we buy a new home, we worry about the price we will sell it for in the future.

You may be surprised to learn that the U.S. divorce rate has actually fallen in the past decade to around 43%. Though it still remains high, we do not have the highest divorce rate in the world. The United Nations reports that Russia, Sweden, Finland and Britain have higher divorce rates than the United States

Why does one in every two marriages fail in the United States? The American divorce rate might be a reflection on how relatively easy it is to get a divorce in the United States. In most states, if the couple has no children, they must be separated six months to a year. However, if children are involved, it could be many years if one partner is unwilling to divorce. State laws vary on the grounds for divorce but most states have "irreconcilable differences." You don't have to explain the circumstances that led you to file for the divorce. You just say you have differences that can't be resolved.

The high divorce rate may also reflect how socially acceptable it is to get a divorce in this country. The social stigma of being divorced is practically gone in the United States, as it was witnessed recently in Southern California. A Volkswagen was decorated with streamers and bright yellow flowers. Painted in big black letters and stuck on the back of the car was a sign "Just Divorced." The woman was honking her horn and waving to people in absolute joy. As people drove past her, they were waving back.

In the United States, after couples divorce, some couples remain friends if they have children. The child spends the week with the Mom and a couple of weekends a month with Dad. The child's bag is usually packed and ready to go to Mom or Dad's house as he or she shuttles back and forth to the parents' homes.

Other single mothers raise their children themselves as many dads disappear after getting divorced. It may be that the mother wants the husband as far away as possible. More often than not, though, it is because the dads do not want to pay the money to support their children or former wife. Dads who disappear in order to escape paying child support or alimony are called *dead-beat dads*.

Not paying child support is such a serious problem for families in this country that many states have recently passed new laws connecting the driver's license data network to court-ordered payments. So if a *dead-beat dad* applies for a driver's license in another state or even renews his license in the same state, the government now has a record of where he lives. If he has been ordered to pay child support, the state will begin to collect child support payments by deducting money from his paycheck.

The U.S. divorce system differs greatly from other countries' practices. In many Muslim countries, divorce is as easy as the man saying he wants a divorce in front of a witness and the couple is divorced. In Japan, being divorced is especially difficult for women, many of whom must find a job for the first time in their lives. Finding an apartment for the divorced partner in such an expensive city such as Tokyo is also another challenge. In Korea, it is common for the husband to get custody of the children of the divorced couple. The husband's parents usually raise the children rather than the mother, as is the custom in the United States.

In other countries with lower divorce rates, living apart without filing divorce papers is more common than here because of the financial or legal burden placed on the divorcing couple. There may be pressure from the family, the religion, or the society not to officially divorce. For whatever reason, couples stay permanently separated without actually filing papers for divorce. In these countries, the permanent separations are not counted as divorce, and in turn, the nation's official divorce rate might be lower than those countries that readily get divorced with papers.

Many people blame our high divorce rate on the fact that 60% of American women work, and therefore fail to balance motherhood with their careers. However difficult it is to maintain this balance, this only partly explains the high divorce rate in the United States

People from other countries often think American women dominate their men in a relationship, but this is more of a media stereotype seen in TV programs than a reflection of the reality. Many married women are independent from their partners rather than dominating them. You see television sitcoms with the woman slapping her husband on the cheek when she is upset by something he said. In the television series *Spin City*, you saw Heather Locklear slapping Michael Fox. In movies, Andie McDowell slapped Bill Murray in *Groundhog Day*, and Gwyneth Paltrow slapped Colin Firth in *Shakespeare in Love*. For entertainment, a woman slapping a man may produce laughs for a sitcom or dramatic tension for a movie. On the screen, the man does not do anything to the woman. But if this happens in real life, a man usually hits back and the woman most often gets hurt.

Historically, American women have been independent from the time the first colonists came to the United States Women often came with their husbands and left their extended family behind in Europe. In rural America, they had no choice but to work alongside their husbands to clear the land, plant food and build houses for themselves and neighbors.

There was a quantum leap in women's independence in the 1940's when American men went to Europe and the Pacific to fight in World War II and women took over men's jobs in factories. When the war was over in 1945 and men returned to reclaim their positions, some women stayed in the working world. Even the women who returned home to be housewives had experienced the world of work for the first time, and many liked it.

The need to work in an undeveloped land and later in factories was followed by the women's rights movement of the 1960's and 1970's. Women no longer felt the social pressure to stay married if it was a bad marriage and filed for divorce in record numbers. Between 1962-1981, the number of divorces tripled in the United States. Birth control and the sexual revolution delivered the final blow to the traditional family. The husband, wife, and two children mold broke into many little pieces, and today families are regrouped into the many unconventional arrangements.

American parents, especially if both mom and dad work, often spend very little time with their children. Instead, they enroll their children in a number of classes. The child plays soccer or Little League or belongs to the Girl Scouts or Boy Scouts. The Mom usually becomes a taxi service dropping off and picking up their children from tutoring, swim class and art class. The only time children have with their parents is often in the car driving somewhere.

Our high divorce rate may have something to do with the fact that we don't want to compromise. Since compromise is required in a marriage, we are faced with a dilemma. We have been raised with the idea that we are the most important creatures on earth. Then we get married and find ourselves called upon to sacrifice for another person. We have also been taught to be self-sufficient since we were little, so we feel guilty if we need someone.

The Western tradition of choosing your own marriage partner based on the falling in love, or what Asians often call "love marriages," is not practiced everywhere in the world. Some families still choose to have arranged marriages in India, Japan, and some Middle Eastern countries. Many Indian families who are living outside of India often wish to marry other Indians. Contrary to popular belief, arranged marriages are usually not forced marriages between strangers today. These marriages are often planned with the consent of the couple, and are a way for parents to actively get involved in choosing a mate for their son or daughter. Families who support arranged marriages claim these kinds of marriages last longer because the backgrounds of the partners are investigated and known beforehand.

Notes

"The thing that impresses me the most about America is the way parents obey their children."

– King Edward VIII, English King (1894-1972)

If you open an American fridge, you'll find...

How We Cook:

We tend to season our food by making it spicier or tastier by adding condiments to the food *after* cooking.

This way, Americans can change the flavor of the food according to their personal taste.

Unlike many other countries, the cook uses seasonings and spices *while* cooking.

- **ketchup – we put it on just about everything.**
- **honey mustard**
- **mayonnaise**
- **soy sauce**
- **salad dressings – two to three bottles.**
- **salsa or hot sauce**
- **steak sauce**

Chapter 5:

Eat Now, Pay Later

W hy are so many Americans overweight? This is the land of light beers, diet Cokes and watery coffee. With so many sugar-free and non-fat foods on our store shelves, we should all be as thin as a pencil.

The paradox is that Americans have a love/hate relationship with food. On one hand, we will eat anything and everything. On the other hand, we feel guilty about most of what we eat. We think about dieting all the time, "I'm on a diet," or "I'm watching my weight," is a permanent fixture in the American mind. It also makes up a good part of our daily conversation. "I know I shouldn't but . . . I don't have much willpower today." For women especially, their self-esteem often depends on how much they weigh.

Sixty percent of American adults are overweight. How Americans became so overweight is complex. It deals with many trends and habits we do not even think about: eating alone, eating fast, and eating while doing another activity.

Frozen food, junk food, fast food, and food associated with fun are some of the reasons for our weight problems.

Eating a meal with someone else is disappearing in the United States. When we eat alone, we eat to fill up our bellies instead of stopping to converse and savor the taste. Many people eat an entire meal in five minutes. We are losing not only our conversational skills, but also our table manners when we eat alone. We lick our fingers, chew with our mouths open, and mix food on our plate in a way we would not normally do in public.

We eat while doing other activities instead of concentrating on the meal. We grab a bowl of cold cereal while reading a newspaper. Some of us don't even take a lunch break. We do errands or eat lunch at our desk. Or we buy take-out from a restaurant and eat our sandwiches while walking back to the office. Others do not get out of their cars at all, but instead, use a drive-thru window of a fast-food restaurant. They order a hamburger and fries and eat their meal while driving.

On the way home from work, many of us buy dinners from the deli section of the grocery store. When we get home, some of us turn on the TV. We may eat dinner watching TV. If we work on the computer in the evening, we may snack while on the computer. Since our minds are not on the food when we eat a meal, we may overeat.

We focus on the quantity of food rather than the quality of the food in the United States. This is reflected in the adage, "the more, the better." At movie theaters, concession stands sell you enormous tubs of popcorn, giant sodas, and monster boxes of candy. Advertisers know how Americans value size. That's why they print the appropriate buzz words on packages to sell their snack foods "Super size," or "Now 50% more." "Two for one specials," "Buy one and get one free," are examples of how we buy food for its quantity.

You can see how Americans value quantity when we order in a restaurant. We frequently ask the waitress about the size of the dish. "How big is it?" We rarely ask whether it's fried, boiled, steamed, whether the dish contains cream or butter, or the kind of seasonings used to make the dish.

These are more quality-type questions, but we are more interested in the quantity of the food. If we did ask questions regarding the quality of the food, the waitress might think we are customers that are hard to please. It wouldn't be surprising if the waitress knows little about the basic methods of preparation or ingredients of a dish, either.

When you order an appetizer or a side dish because you want a small portion, the server will look at you strangely or your friends will even pressure you to have a full meal. Many people who want less food make up a medical excuse. "I can't eat this or that because I'm on medication," or "I just ate a huge breakfast or lunch."

So you order in a restaurant and your plate comes to your table. The food is piled up as high as Mount Fuji. Restaurants often serve enough food for three people in one order. This makes us feel good. First, we feel good that we are unable to eat it all. We can ask for a doggie bag to take the rest home. Some of us eat the food in the doggie bag as soon as we get home. We feel guilty about eating it all in front of everyone in the restaurant, or maybe we were full before, but twenty minutes have gone by and our needs have changed. A smaller number of us save it for tomorrow's lunch or dinner. This also makes us feel good as we feel there is value in eating out. We have just spent our money in a restaurant not for one meal but for a meal and a half.

Americans are also overweight because they snack between meals. Snacks are everywhere. Overweight people fail to stop munching on snacks when they want to lose weight. They simply buy snack food that is fat-free, salt-free or sweetened with a no calorie sweetener instead of sugar.

There is a non-fat potato chip bag that lets people eat the whole bag for 0 grams of fat. So Americans have the notion they are eating less. Only 200 calories for the whole bag of potato chips! They eat the whole bag. You see this logic in fast food places too. People order a hamburger, a large fries and a giant *diet* Coke.

Americans buy junk food because it's cheaper. Why is it that a bag of apples cost more than one huge bag of doughnuts? Or a liter of Coke is less expensive than a small bottle of water? If something is too expensive, Americans won't buy it. Seafood is one example. Many Americans like seafood but do not often buy it because the price is out of reach.

In lower-income neighborhoods and inner cities, you only find expensive convenience stores like a *7-11*. We seldom see grocery stores with fresh fruit and vegetables. Coupons in the local newspaper are mainly for packaged, canned, frozen or junk foods. There are never coupons for discounts on fresh fruit and vegetables.

Food has been taken out of the area of nourishment for the body and into the universe of entertainment. Food is fun. Advertisers shape and package food into something that looks like a toy. There are purple and green crackers shaped like goldfish. We have green ketchup and blue Pepsi. We have peanut butter and jelly swirls in a jar. Breakfast cereals are coated with peanut butter and chocolate and taste more like candy than cereal. Cereal boxes hide toys at the bottom. McDonald's and Burger King give away dolls and action figures so children will beg their parents to go to their fast food outlets for the toy.

Our top athletes add to the fun element by selling all kinds of food ranging from Coca-cola to sugar-laden breakfast food. Tennis star Serena Williams promotes hamburgers for McDonald's. Kobe Bryant pitches Coca Cola. NASCAR's race car driver Jeff Gordon promotes Frito corn chips, "Fun Food for the Fast Lane." Gordon is also on Frosted Mini-Wheats cereal boxes for Kellogg.

Cooking: The Million-Dollar Question

Why don't Americans cook? Americans *don't* cook rather than *can't* cook. They could cook if they took the time but few people actually do. Some people think of cooking as a time-consuming activity that nobody appreciates anyway. It is true that many young people grow up on restaurant food and the microwave and so have no cooking skills, but the middle-aged usually know how to cook but choose not to. They may also compare their cooking to the ethnic restaurants they have at their disposal and say why bother? You see this attitude at potlucks or our famous bring your own dish parties. In the past, people used to bring homemade dishes but now you mostly see dishes from the deli section of a grocery store.

How are cookbooks best sellers in the United States yet most Americans seldom cook a homemade meal? Many of us have these handsomely-illustrated cookbooks on our coffee tables. We openly display them on kitchen shelves, enjoy them for casual reading at night to "know" more about food theoretically, and we often pull the cookbook out for a holiday recipe. Even on holidays, though, many Americans go out to eat or order prepared food from a grocery store, deli or restaurant.

While few parents are passing on their cooking skills to their children, most schools today have no classes on how to cook either. Twenty-five years ago, schools made their junior-high school students take a class called home economics. It was a class that taught basic cooking methods and where students practiced making a variety of dishes. Today, schools offer an elective class called life skills, which is similar to the home economics class of the past.

When you go into an American grocery store, delis compete with restaurants, as more Americans are eating out today. To encourage you to buy on a subconscious level, some supermarkets roast chicken all day on the grill so the chicken smells will whet your appetite, and in turn, cause you to buy more food.

Food in this country is very convenient. Entire meals are frozen for you. International visitors visit a supermarket and are shocked at the aisles of frozen food. The need to transport food from one part of the country to another arose in the 1930's and the idea of frozen food was born. Then the microwave oven came into existence in the 1970's. This invention shrank the preparation time of heating up a frozen food tray in the conventional oven and took convenience to new heights. It no longer takes forty minutes in a regular oven. Now we can have our food ready in a microwave minute.

Who actually eats these frozen foods? Many people buy frozen food because they are pressed for time. Such people range from college students who lack kitchen facilities to people who are on diets. Those trying to lose weight often buy a Weight Watchers food tray or a Healthy Choice Gourmet. They pop these instant meals into the microwave for lunch and know exactly how many calories they are consuming for their calorie-restricted diet. In this way, dieters don't have to worry about portion control. Frozen meals like the Stouffers food trays provide dinner for many of our elderly who live alone. Senior citizens eat these meals because they want to be as independent as possible yet do not want to cook.

Tempting food smells are everywhere in the United States. The smell of grease from the frying of hamburgers and french fries can be sniffed as you pass the local McDonald's or Burger King. Food smells are entering cosmetics and toys. Shampoos and body creams are fruit-scented and kid's magic markers smell like lemons, strawberries and grapes.

Food and Additives

Why is our food so full of chemicals or additives? Makers of orange juice put enough vitamin C in a glass of orange juice so you don't need to eat another fruit all day.

What is boxed cereal doing with a daily supply of calcium without the milk anyway? "Enriched" is a euphemism meaning full of additives.

Many foods have high fructose sweeteners or corn syrup added for no apparent reason. Corn syrup is a by-product of processed corn. Since the United States is a major producer of corn, this cheap by-product is put into every imaginable food possible. Juices that come in a carton have corn syrup as the primary sweetener. Ketchup, cold cereals, snack crackers, tomato sauce, yogurt, and a wide variety of foods also contain this syrup.

Exercise

Lack of exercise contributes to our weight problems. The United States has two extremes: exercise fanatics or couch potatoes. The exercise conscious run a few miles every day or go to the gym to keep in shape. The opportunities to exercise are plentiful. Twenty-four hour fitness clubs dot the landscape, and public parks give us enough space to do any exercise we can imagine.

Eating less and exercising more costs nothing, but Americans typically think of spending money in order to shed those pounds. We join a health club, hire a personal trainer, and buy a Stairmaster that takes up the whole living room. We purchase Nike exercise clothes instead of walking or biking with our families. We eat pre-packaged frozen diet foods, diet snacks, and vitamin pills instead of simply consuming less food.

Fourteen percent of American children are overweight, too. Schools sell junk food in vending machines and get a percentage of the soda and fast-food sales. Since schools are always in need of money, this is an easy way to make money without doing any fund raising. It is encouraging to see that some parents have criticized this practice saying it leads to obesity in children, and a few schools have changed. School districts in New York City and San

What Is American Food?

(not just hamburgers and hot dogs)

How we turn food from other countries into blurry photocopies of the originals.

Sushi into California Rolls

In the U.S., we took Japanese sushi and made it with less raw fish and stuffed it with more avocado, imitation crab and colorful vegetables. In Japan, the outside of rolled sushi is usually seaweed, but Americans have put the rice on the outside.

Tortillas into Fast Tacos & Burritos

The simple unfried tortilla, which is usually served with a Mexican meal, has undergone a frying fiesta in the U.S. We took the tortillas, fried them, and added an enormous amount of cheese and sour cream.

These lunchtime favorites have changed Mexican plain and basic tortillas into rich, fast-food sandwiches bearing the names of *burritos and enchiladas*.

Francisco have banned the vending machines in elementary schools.

American Food

What is American food? Is it only hamburgers and hot dogs?

Americans copy food from every country you can think of. Immigrants come here with native recipes and good intentions of making the identical dish here. It's like putting an authentic, detailed recipe in the photocopy machine. *Voila*! A simplified version of the dish comes out the other end.

Unfortunately, the dish is missing key ingredients because they aren't available in the United States. Americans usually want to shorten the cooking and preparation methods. The result comes out tasting quite different from the native dish and foreigners easily recognize the difference in taste. This is not Chinese or Italian food. It's the American version of it. You can find these copycats of international cuisine in restaurants throughout the United States. Even in small towns, there is at least one Chinese or Italian restaurant somewhere. But take note, you will usually eat the altered photocopy version, not the original.

A teacher's visit to Scripps Aquarium with international students revealed strong cultural differences regarding food. The Japanese students peered into the tanks and politely pointed out how delicious the octopus, squid and other fish species were. To them, the beauty and mystery of coral reefs and fauna were nice, but concentrating on the fish as an edible source of food was better.

Despite the internationalization of food, the rich cuisine of a particular region of the country is still very much alive in the United States. You can find clam chowder in Boston, Cajun stew in Louisiana, Soul food, or grits and greens in the South, and Tex-Mex food in the Southwest. Many

Italian Pizza into Party Food

In Italy, the most common pizza is a thin 10-inch round tomato and cheese pizza for one person called the *margarita*.

○ Here we have taken this simple tomato and cheese pizza and made it into California cuisine by putting a variety of toppings on our pizza such as broccoli, sausage, anchovies and pineapple.

○ Some Americans even put ketchup on pizza. Pizza is bigger here and comes divided into many slices. Because it's cheap and filling meal, it has become a party favorite.

Chinese Fortune Cookies

These famous cookies were invented in the United States, though there is still some mystery surrounding the origin.

The Chinese '49'ers working on the railroad exchanged these cookies with happy messages inside. They are said to be American copies of Chinese mooncakes.

Sweet Bread into Gooey Doughnuts

Doughnuts are a popular to-go breakfast in the United States. Are doughnuts considered dessert or breakfast foods?

We have taken sweet bread, which is seen in many countries for breakfast, and have put every imaginable filling into them and icing on top of them. Then we have renamed them doughnuts.

Americans also grow up eating the food of their grandparents. If your family has Polish and Italian ancestry, for example, then you probably grew up eating sausage and spaghetti. Food customs are the most enduring foreign customs preserved in the United States.

Of course, there are also the meat and potatoes and the overcooked vegetable as a typical meal. American food is usually seasoned with only a little salt and pepper in the preparation. This is why it is considered bland to most foreigners, or even "tasteless."

Although we use very few spices and seasonings *during* the cooking process, we change the flavor *after* with condiments. We pour dressings, ketchup, mustard, soy sauce, Worcestershire sauce, mayonnaise, and hot sauce to improve the flavor of the food. This is the American's way of seasoning food. We make our food as sweet, salty, or spicy as we want. It's not left to the discretion of the cook but a matter of personal choice for the person who eats the food.

It is also typically American that few holidays are tied to a particular food in the United States as they are in other countries. We have no special food for birthdays, funerals or remembering our ancestors as many other countries do. Thanksgiving might be the exception as most people still have turkey, sweet potatoes and cranberry sauce. Many people have eggnog for New Year's Eve and American children go trick or treating for candy on Halloween. We have barbecues for Memorial and Labor Day. However, there are no rituals regarding the preparation of the food, its significance, or the order in which we eat the particular food on these holidays.

English:
The Beauty & the Beast

English is easier to read and write than to speak since it has 26 letters but the actual number of sounds is 35 (11 vowels and 24 consonant sounds).

○ **One English word can have many meanings.**

- You rock! (rock is a slangy adjective to mean great) "She rocks the baby," (rock as a verb); "He threw a rock at her," (rock as a noun); "I listen to rock," (rock as a noun).

○ **New expressions are added quickly** by combining existing language elements or combining a verb with a preposition such as "hang out," "drop off," "hand in" and attaching prefixes to existing verbs: "upload," "offbeat" and "downplay."

○ **English takes from other languages:**

- **French:** action, air, adventure, count, justice
- **African:** cola, banana, yam, gorilla, jazz, banjo
- **Italian:** piano, umbrella, volcano, artichoke
- **Persian:** paradise, chess, check, and lemon
- **Chinese:** ketchup, silk, tea, chopstick, soy, wok
- **Arabic:** almanac, cotton, orange, sugar, syrup
- **Portuguese:** stereo, monsoon, stead, safari
- **German:** flak, iceberg, cookbook
- **Hindi:** caste, bazaar
- **Japanese:** judo, bonsai, sushi, origami, karaoke

Chapter 6:

English as an Only Language

W hy don't Americans learn a second language? The United States is a leader in international politics and economics yet is one of the most monolingual nations in the world. The answer lies in the roots of American history and geography. We have a history of Americanizing foreigners by making them give up their language and speak English.

The original Americans, the Native Americans, had hundreds of languages, 200 of which still survive today. When the white settlers came west and settled on their lands, Indian tribes moved further west, until eventually there was no more land to move to. The United States government resettled the different tribes into reservations, or they were killed. In the late 19th century, the U.S. government took Indian children away from their parents on the reservations, and put them into boarding schools to force them to assimilate. There, Christian missionaries cut off their long hair, took their tribal clothes, put them in uniform, and forced them to speak English. Indian children were punished if they spoke their own language. Over time, these tribal languages, which were mainly oral languages, have been lost as elders die. Native Americans, in other words, were "Americanized."

Tribal languages, however, left their cultural imprint on the U.S. map. The names of half of the fifty states come from Indian languages. Massachusetts means "at or about the great hill," Illinois is "tribe of superior men," Connecticut signifies "beside the long tidal river." Colonialists needed new words to describe the new animals they met and so took the Indian words *raccoon, caribou, moose, skunk* and *woodchuck*, and English grew.

Just as Indian tribes had many languages, so did black slaves when they came to the United States from Africa. Blacks couldn't speak to each other in their African tongues because slaves were brought from several nations and tribes. In order to survive, slaves learned to communicate through a few slave preachers literate enough to get words from the Bible and house servants who had contact with whites. A kind of abbreviated English with West African language structure developed. This was the root of Black English today.

Black English has given us many words. *Jazz* is a West African term, and *hip, dig* (understand or appreciate) *banjo, tote, yam, zombie* and *bug* (annoy), *guy*, and *bogus* (false).

African Americans often use words with the opposite meaning because in the past, blacks had to encode their language to survive in front of whites. For instance, *bad* is *good* and *kill* means strongly affect someone. These kinds of words were born in America and set American English apart from other countries whose native language is English.

Today, Americans still struggle with the language issue as the number of foreign-born has sharply increased in the last decade. Today, each state determines whether it will have bilingual classes, English as a second language classes, or both. Bilingual classes are classes that are conducted in the immigrant's language, while the student takes English as a second language. During the 2-5 years of bilingual education classes, students are gradually immersed into English classes until they have classes only in English. To further complicate the school language problem, critics of bilingual education believe this method of learning just postpones learning English.

As new immigrants arrive, new laws are made to protect English. The United States started its English language laws state by state in the 1870s in response to the large waves of immigrants from Poland and Italy. Theodore Roosevelt said "Every immigrant here should be required to learn English within five years or leave the country." Today, of the one million immigrants that arrive in the United States each year, a half million legally and an estimated half million illegally, most are Spanish-speakers.

Twenty-five states have passed English Only laws. This means state governments will no longer print voting ballots, driver's license tests, medical documents and other government documents in foreign languages. Many immigrant groups have protested, saying this denies them equal access to voting, driving, and medical care.

In the workplace, we are divided too. Some employers discourage their employees from speaking another language other than English. On the other hand, retail stores welcome the Hispanic dollar. Bilingual sales clerks are hired and valued because they can wait on a Spanish-speaking customer and increase sales.

Owning the Language

Who owns the language? Is it the government which makes laws telling us which language to use? Or is it the people who use English and change it to meet their needs?

While Americans debate whether they should speak another language, foreigners are increasingly learning

English worldwide. People using English as a second language now outnumber native speakers. There are about 350 million native English speakers compared to 500 million second language speakers. Add all the countries that speak English as a foreign language and it comes to nearly one billion English speakers or nearly one in every seven people on the planet speaks English. It is the primary language of science, computers and business. English is being spoken in Asia as a common business language among the Japanese, Koreans, and the Chinese. The same is true in Mexico and Brazil, where European, Japanese and Korean investment is growing.

English creeps into other languages. Japanese, German, and French have seen an influx of English in their languages. In some countries, English is used as a status symbol, a way to show that you are a member of the elite or have studied in the United States. Yet, English is not always welcomed abroad, as illustrated by the French government. It has recently banned English words from advertising, the media, and official documents in an attempt to keep French pure and intact.

English borrows from other languages too. English is growing so fast because it seldom rejects foreign words for purity reasons. John Adams, one of our country's founders, suggested creating an American Academy of English to keep the language free from a foreign invasion of words back in 1780. No one listened to him at the time. Consequently, the United States has no group of linguistic scholars combing every word to see if it qualifies as proper English, unlike the "language watchdogs" of France and Spain.

New English words are coined relatively quickly from other languages as immigrants come to the United States. Language and culture cannot be isolated. You can see how the cultural interaction between foreigners and Americans influences English to the extent that it borrows from the new language at the expense of an English word. We use *kaput* from German, *déjà vu* from French, *kudos* from Greek, *kimono* from Japanese, *karma* from Sanskrit and *ketchup* from Cantonese. These foreign words are eventually adopted into the English sound system and make their way into an American English dictionary.

The English language loves brevity and new abbreviations are born as language incorporates new phenomenon. For example, CDs are not only *Certificates of Deposits* but also *compact discs*. PCs could be *personal computers* or *politically correct*.

English is growing as we use English in new ways and create more euphemisms so we do not offend anyone. These shades of meaning are often hard to identify by the international visitor. We use *significant other* to describe a boyfriend or girlfriend outside of traditional family patterns.

Sales associate sounds more prestigious than sales clerk. We are not *at war* but *engaged* in a country. We no longer have a *confrontation* with a person but an *incident*, and the list goes on. English is growing at a rate of a thousand words a year, says Richard Lederer in *The Miracle of Language*. All these new words make their way into the Webster's International Dictionary, bulging at 450,000 words.

Because English is growing and so widely practiced, Americans see little need to learn a foreign language. For their customary two-week vacations, most Americans go to another state or city within the United States instead of traveling to a foreign country. This is why Americans fail to understand the value of learning another language. Census data reveals only 8% of children 5 to 17 years old speak another language other than English at home and most of these children are from foreign-born parents who have kept their language.

Forty percent of high school students study a foreign language, yet few speak another language after two to four years of study. Spanish is by far the most popular choice. Americans have taken an interest in learning Spanish ever since advertising agencies began marketing to Hispanics in their language on TV, billboards and the radio.

When Americans travel to Texas, Florida, or Southern California where Spanish is widely spoken, they feel excluded. The irony is that Americans want to learn Spanish to speak with more people *within* their country and not to understand people from *other* countries.

Spanish is primarily a spoken language in the United States. Since many Spanish speakers who were born and raised here were not schooled in the reading or writing of the language, the written form of the mother tongue has been nearly lost. It's like an adopted daughter because we seldom see Spanish written except on billboards or government documents.

The Spanish you hear in Spain and the Spanish you hear in the United States are completely different since the language has become Americanized. We mix English with Spanish all the time. We name this hybrid language Spanglish. We have many nationalities speaking the language here so each ethnic group speaks it differently but all mix it with English.

Americans view culture with blinders on. We have forced immigrants to give up their language but then we celebrate Hispanic Month, African American Month, and Native American month. We charge money to see ethnic groups dance and serve their food at local fairs and school functions. Performing a dance and bringing a dish are acceptable ways to celebrate cultural heritage. In short, the message is clear in America. Show us a foreign culture through food and dance, but not language.

Notes

"We don't just borrow words; on occasion, English has pursued other languages down alleyways to beat them unconscious and rifle their pockets for new vocabulary."

– Booker T. Washington,
American black leader and educator
(1856-1915)

How Do We Make Friends?

Let me count the 16 ways...

E-mail Friend

Bus Friend

Study Partner

Work Friend

True Friend

Tennis Partner

Roommate

Gym Friend

Teammate

Sweetheart

Neighbor

Lunch Partner

Chess Partner

Family Friend

Classmate

Travelmate

Chapter 7:

True Friends

W hy is it so difficult to make friends with Americans? Many international visitors complain about how superficial Americans are. It's true that after years of knowing people in the United States, you may never be invited to their home. This is unthinkable in other countries.

You have to understand how Americans categorize you, the friend. Many people from other countries misinterpret *being friendly* with *being a friend*.

Being friendly means Americans are easy to approach.

We are open to striking up conversations with a stranger in the grocery line, on the bus or just about anywhere in public. We usually don't ask the stranger's name. The public place simply serves the function of a temporary friendship that dissolves immediately after the chance encounter.

This friendliness also means that if we know you, we might pat you on the back if you are a man, or hug you if you are a woman. Between young people of both sexes, you might be asked to slap the open palm of your hand of another person, "Give me five!" Or you might greet the other person with "a knuckle handshake." The old-fashioned handshake is going out of style for personal encounters among friends, but is still practiced for introductions and business relationships.

Many people from other countries are surprised to see how informal we are. Americans easily put their feet up on a desk or chair, sit down on a table instead of a chair, or even go to a store dressed in what could be called pajamas.

Americans love their space, and might overlook other people's needs when they sit or stand. You can see examples of this by how one person may claim two seats on the bus, in the classroom, or the movie theater. One seat is for the person, while the other seat is for their belongings.

When Americans are introduced to each other and the meeting is intentional, we want to know the other person's name right away. Since we don't have titles for most people in the United States, the name becomes the most important factor in identifying a person.

Americans generally dislike personal titles, as we were the nation of rebels that protested against the royalty and the Church of England. In the times of slavery, slaves had to call their white owners "Master." They also were forced to say "Yes Ma'am" and "No Ma'am," and "Yes Sir," and "No Sir," to all whites as a sign of deference to them.

Today, people from the South still retain the "Sir" and "Ma'am" custom, and it has become a polite-sounding tradition to their ears. The American military also retains this form of address as a sign of respect to authority.

We can trace the titles of "Sir" and "Ma'am" to the Middle Ages. Back in the times of 1100-1400, La Dame was a title reserved for women of refinement. La Dame was shortened to Madame, which became later shortened to Ma'am. The male equivalent for a dame was a knight, and was called Sire, which was shortened to Sir. In a formal letter when we don't know a person's name, we still write, "Dear Sir or Madam."

However, to Americans of the North, Midwest, and West, calling them "Sir" and "Ma'am" sounds old-fashioned and too formal. It usually makes them feel uncomfortable because it sounds like one person is putting the other person in a lower position. It goes against the tradition of people considering themselves equal. And if you say "Ma'am" to most women, you will offend them, as many women think this title makes them feel old.

Vestiges of the Middle Ages can also be seen in our notion of "being a gentleman." Chivalry was a code of conduct created by the knights of the Middle Ages to protect the weak, at that time including women, from the warrior class. Today, chivalry is a kind of etiquette that is practiced by men and grants women common courtesies in the United States. For example, it can be pulling out a chair for a woman at dinner, walking on the street side of a sidewalk, opening a door and letting her go into the building first, or giving up a seat on a bus. Feminists dislike this special treatment and say it reinforces the inequality of gender.

What titles do we commonly use in the United States? Some religious, academic, and legal titles are still practiced. Physicians and college PhD's are still called "Doctor." Students of all ages usually address their teachers as Mr. and Miss followed by the last name until they graduate from high school. In court, the judge is still called "Your Honor."

For religious leaders, we still use "Pastor, Father, Rabbi and Imam."

Since many Americans do not have their parents and siblings close by, sometimes they have their children call unrelated close friends with the artificial title of Aunt and Uncle before their first name. This practice is common when close friends serve as a kind of surrogate family.

Yet we don't have titles to express the nuances of relationship with other people, as some cultures do. What

Culture: USA

1. **Go to a local high school football or basketball game** and root with the acrobatic cheerleaders.

2. **Take a mini-road trip** to a tourist attraction and stop at a roadside diner.

3. **Order a banana split** at an ice-cream shop.

4. **Watch a live trial** in a local criminal courthouse.

5. **Stop by a local taco shop at night** and ask for a *burrito de carne asada*.

6. **See a house on wheels** by going into a mobile home park and asking to see the inside of a model.

7. **Make a campfire in the countryside** and sing camp songs while roasting marshmallows.

8. **Jog around your neighborhood** in the early morning and see serious dog walkers and runners.

9. **Organize a potluck dinner** at home with no fuss as everyone brings a "pot"or dish to eat.

10. **Have a tailgate party** by packing up your car with picnic food and chairs and having a party in the parking lot before an American game starts.

about strangers? What do you call the person who forgot her bag on the bus and is now 100 feet (30 meters) away?

Or the waitress you have patiently waited for but now feel the need to call her attention? Or what about the person sitting next to you in class who wants to be your friend? What about a special name for your boss, your grandmother or even your mother-in-law?

Unfortunately, we have only one *you* in English. *You* for an individual, *you* for a group, *you* for the president and you for the guy next door. We don't have special verb forms or titles to distinguish age, class, stranger, or familiar. That's why your given name becomes all important in American culture. If Americans do not get your name at a party or personal setting, they most likely won't talk to you for any length of time.

If we need to call someone whose name we do not know, and they are far away, we call them by function or identify them by the clothing they wear. We raise our voice and say, "Excuse me, lady in the white dress!" Or, "Excuse me, waitress!" These name and title rules in the United States bring us back to the friendship question. Americans think of friendship in a very superficial and functional way.

Once Americans know your name and something personal about you, you are usually considered a friend. We have the term "acquaintance" in the English language, but we seldom use it.

Americans make friends easily but it is a rather functional relationship. We put friends in boxes according to where we see them and by the activity shared with them.

If we play tennis, we have a tennis friend. If we know someone at school, we become a school friend. It follows then that we have church friends, family friends, and work friends.

Church friends are rarely invited to play tennis, and tennis friends do not go to church with us. Seldom do we invite one set of friends home to mix with family friends. The friend is in a box with a label on it, "Tennis," "Church," and "Work," and we stow the friend away to be taken out for that one activity.

This functional approach to friendship results in making many friends but knowing few of them well.

Americans move an average of 11 times in a lifetime. The unknown future is always more exciting than today, which may be too familiar. New is equivalent to better in the mind of Americans. We move to get a *better*, not *different*, roommate, job or house. As a result, many Americans keep a distance and choose not to invest the time and the energy needed to build a friendship. Why should I get close to people if they will move away in a couple of years?

Obviously, this presents a particular problem for foreign students and visitors. In the United States for only a short time, meeting Americans usually isn't as much of a problem as getting to know them on a deeper level.

Americans know that the international visitor will leave in the near future, and this will make them very conscious of the amount of time and emotional energy spent on making friends. They might appear warm until the visitor wants to get close to them and then Americans will take a step back. *Not too close.* We might get hurt when the visitor moves away or returns home.

Whatever favors *you do for someone* or whatever favors *you ask of someone* are mentally recorded in an American's mind like a debit or credit card. Simple daily needs that are met by other people have turned into unwritten commercial transactions.

Favors count like money and trading favors is the currency. If you ask an American for a ride in his/her car one day, it is expected that you will do something for that person in the future. If an American invites you to his/her home, you are expected to invite him/her home back at a future date, or at least out to eat. We know we owe someone a favor and must repay him with some kind of favor. We say, "I'm paying you back for the ride you gave me the other day." Or if we haven't done someone a favor yet, we might say, "I owe you."

We are very specific about what we do for others and what people do not do for us. Friendship in this way has become a very commercial idea that most Americans aren't even conscious of. Or, if we are aware of it, we think it is just "being fair." If you do not repay an American you have asked many favors from, the American might feel used, and you might even lose the American friend. On the other hand, if we have asked too many favors of you and realize it, Americans tend to feel guilty and apologize.

With time and persistence, foreigners do make friends with Americans despite the unwritten rules governing friendship. If you do many kinds of activities with an American, including going to each other's house and knowing each other's family, then you are probably considered a "close friend" or maybe a "best friend." You have managed to jump out of the box and transcend the idea of a functional friend. You are able to judge how clean or messy we are, what personal habits we have and what we hang on our walls. Americans think all of this is highly personal and brings friendship to a different level.

Friendship has become a business in the United States in another sense, too, as the word *friendly* is used as a marketing term. It is used to describe who is welcome in a place and who is not. For example, we have restaurants and hotels with signs posted *child-friendly*, which means children are welcome. States are using *business-friendly* to say that their particular state is a good place to do business, with low corporate tax rates, low wages, or few unions. The term *user-friendly* is used for computer interfaces, and even appliances when the machine is easy to use. *Environmental-friendly* is a widely-used term seen on plastic containers that are biodegradable. This term is also used by cosmetic companies such as the Body Shop, a company that does not use animal testing. Can you imagine a Statue of Liberty saying *foreigner-friendly* today?

Chapter 8:

Crazy for Rules

If this is the land of the free, then why are there so many rules? Do Americans really think they are free with so many laws telling them what they can and cannot do?

Yes, we love to make laws in the United States. We usually make new ones when a private corporation has been sued too many times or some major accident has happened.

Smoking laws were passed when the cigarette maker R.J. Reynolds was slapped with enough lawsuits, safety belts were required after enough accidents, and the age to drink was changed when the number of young people killed in drunk driving accidents rose.

The United States has the most lawyers in the world. We also have one of the highest numbers of people in jail on the planet. We have about 2 million prisoners in jail. Many of these prisoners are not serious criminals but non-violent drug offenders. It costs at least $20,000 a year to house each inmate. Everything we do in the United States has a legal consequence. People walk around in fear. If we break the law, we are afraid someone will either sue us or report us to the police.

Lawsuits arise out of the most ordinary events. When passengers were afraid during a rough American Airlines flight from Los Angeles to New York, they sued the airlines for emotional damages and were awarded $2 million dollars. When an Ohio coach for a Little League baseball team had no wins for the team for the entire season, the father of one of the kids sued the coach for poor coaching. In an Arizona high school, the parents of an English student threatened to sue the school when her daughter failed her English class, so just hours before graduation, the girl was allowed to retake a multiple-choice test. The student barely passed, and was permitted to graduate.

As you can see, making mistakes in daily life here can be not only costly but also turned into a lawsuit in the United States. This is why most Americans, driven by fear of jail or a lawsuit, obey the laws in this country.

Morality is encoded in our civil laws. Rules are posted on signs like the Ten Commandments in the Bible. "No Trespassing" means you can't go on this property. Even if there is no fence, the legal result is the same to an American. You are breaking the law. "No Loitering" means you are not allowed to stay around a store's entrance or parking lot unless you are a customer.

Of course, we are all aware of the no smoking laws. If we aren't, Americans quickly point to the sign and ask, "Did you read the sign?" This is American logic. If the sign is posted, you are informed, and so you will naturally follow the rules.

Drinking Laws

We can drive at age 16, vote at 18, and drink at 21. Drinking must be considered the best as it is saved for last. We can kill someone in a car or get killed in a car accident at 16, we can kill and get killed in the military at 18 but at 21, we can legally have that beer! Now that's a paradox.

Why is this? The reality is that young people under 21 years old *do drink and drive.* The law is made to separate the two activities, drinking and driving, in order to prevent fatal car accidents among young people. The law wasn't meant for the government to be the moral police but to reduce the number of fatal accidents.

What alternatives are there to driving at night in the United States if you want to drink alcohol? It looks pretty grim. In most cities, somewhat undependable local buses mostly stop running in the early evenings and have limited schedules on weekends. Friends can help a little by going along with you and not drinking so they can drive you home. Taxis are usually too expensive to be considered a practical alternative by young people when they drink.

Americans' moral sentiments run strong when it comes to underage drinking and driving. Yet many adults serve alcohol to their teens at home. In fact, many cities have laws that make serving alcohol to underage people at home a crime. Parents or any adult can face a $1,000 fine and up to six months in jail for hosting parties where alcohol was served to underage kids.

Prohibiting drinking until 21 has produced a pattern of drinking that is uniquely American. It is not found in other countries, even though they have a lower drinking age limit. Drinking is more exciting when it's illegal. Not only do American young people drink in their cars and in parking lots, but they also drink with the goal of getting drunk. Since students are not allowed to drink three of their four years in college, drinking privately in your own apartment is fairly common. Young people not only drink secretly but some drink five or more alcoholic drinks in one sitting. This is called binge drinking, and it is pretty common on college campuses. American teenagers have never learned to drink in a social setting so when we finally reach 21 and drink, it turns out to be a selfish kind of pleasure. It is often a means to get drunk rather than a way to socialize.

The Legal System

Our legal system is a mystery to many foreign visitors as they watch famous legal movies such as *A Few Good Men*, *Witness*, or *Dead Man Walking*. Unlike most real trials, movies and TV programs are full of high drama and well-spoken lawyers.

Very few criminal cases actually go to trial, with an estimated 90% being settled by a plea bargain. A plea bargain is an agreement between the district attorney and the defense about the charges. The defendant enters a guilty plea and a sentence is administered, all without a trial.

The small percent of cases that do go to trial are what you read about in the newspapers. Most trials are open to the public, so ordinary citizens can walk into any courtroom and watch the legal process in action. Unlike television shows depicting a courtroom full of people, most American courtrooms are empty except for a few close friends or relatives of the defendant. Of course, in a highly publicized case of a celebrity, the major media are there. Then the courtroom is crowded and sometimes the trial is televised.

Who makes up a jury? Local residents of the city are called for jury duty. It is an obligation of every adult American citizen to serve on a jury. People's names are randomly chosen from voting and driver's license lists.

Nearly every adult is called to jury duty at least once in his or her lifetime. Nearly everyone tries to get out of it, too.

People dislike going because it can mean taking from two weeks to several months off work to serve on a trial jury. As a potential juror, you have no idea how long the trial will last. Even selecting a jury could take days. Few employers pay for the time served on a jury. The companies that do provide a jury service benefit usually pay your salary for a maximum of two weeks. The court gives jurors a few dollars a day to pay for transportation and/or lunch money.

Naturally, this virtually unpaid civic duty competes with income-earning jobs, and our jobs usually win. Many Americans write elaborate excuses so they will be excused for jury duty. Others try to get out of jury duty by showing up on the first day of jury selection and answering questions in a way that lawyers will not select them to be a member of the jury. Because of the number of people trying to escape jury duty by the lengthy selection process, many states have new rules that say a jury must be selected in one day.

Race may play a role in producing jury verdicts or the decisions of guilty or not guilty. The highly-publicized Rodney King trial of 1992 is an example. An all-white jury acquitted four white police officers. A predominantly black jury acquitted O.J. Simpson, a famous black athlete accused of murdering his wife and his wife's friend. When a white jury tried Simpson in civil court later, he was found guilty.

Owning Guns

Why do Americans own 65 million handguns? Americans cite the Constitution like no other country in the world. The question should be, why is the murder rate so high in the United States? You can't assume the United States has a high murder rate because so many Americans own guns. It ignores the mentality of Americans and their idea of safety.

Is owning a gun the cause for the high murder rate? An international study on guns and crime in 21 countries found that gun ownership was high in Switzerland, Finland and Canada, but their murder rates were much lower than the United States. But the study also found that guns in the home may lead to suicide, and that they are a threat to women, especially female partners. Owning a gun, however, has little relationship to the murder rates for males or street crime.

Nearly half of the murders in the United States are committed by people who are acquainted with their victims, reports the Bureau of Justice in its 2000 *Homicide Trends in the U.S.* report. *Now that's frightening.* It seems that focusing on guns without finding out why Americans are killing people who are their acquaintances, co-workers and family members is a futile exercise.

Blaming the lack of a conventional family structure does not explain it entirely. Sweden has twice as many births outside marriage than the United States and Canada has about the same as the United States and these countries' murder rates are a fraction of the American murder rate.

Something else causes people to murder other people besides the convenience of owning a gun or the fact that we have many unconventional families.

The high murder rate may be connected to the large gap between the rich and the poor compared to other industrialized countries. The poor and the nonwhite are more likely to be targets of a violent crime than the rich and white. Blacks are almost six times as likely to be murder victims as whites, according to the Bureau of Justice in its 2000 *Homicide Trends in the U.S.* report.

It's clear that Americans feel unsafe in their own country, but this fear is abstract. We have no one in particular in mind. Gun owners argue that they own guns for self-defense. Because the police cannot cover all situations, gun owners say, they are supplementing government protection. Gun supporters also say that owning a gun provides low-income people with a means for self-protection. It's cheaper than an expensive alarm system for a house or the cost of maintaining a security dog. So is it the burglars we are worried about? Then why are students carrying guns to school? With 10% of the schools in the United States reporting serious violence, fear of burglars is a questionable argument.

College students now carry guns too. When polled for

the reason college students needed a gun, they said "for self-defense." Against whom? Anybody? This notion of carrying a gun because you are afraid of someone is becoming more widespread. Thirty-one states have right-to-carry laws allowing people to carry a concealed gun on their person.

What we say and what we do are often two different things. We say we want safer cities, but what are we doing to solve the high crime rate? As a culture, we concentrate on the technology, so we say let's get rid of the machinery or the guns and not deal with changing our ideas about violence.

Violent movies such as *Diehard* and *Armageddon* gross millions and qualify as blockbusters in the United States. The culture of violence is built into our American mentality.

We have not learned to resolve conflicts through negotiation and complex talks. We do not know how to manage our anger. When we are mad, we like action, not words. When we kill someone with a gun, the problem is solved in a simple way. After all, that's how movies get rid of the bad guys.

We idolize the cowboy; the loner who has been wronged and waits for no one to help him but takes justice into his own hands. The quick and easy solution in a complex world has turned this country into a people who look to take personal revenge to its extreme of killing, with no chance of that person ever coming back to take revenge on you.

The Death Penalty

Why does the United States have the death penalty? The argument that the death penalty prevents murder is a myth.

With that reasoning, having the death penalty in 38 of the 50 states would make the United States the safest country on the planet. We know that's not true.

Some Americans support the death penalty because

they are afraid that criminals sent to prison for life will eventually get out of jail based on their good behavior. This rarely happens today, as we have life sentences without parole. This means there is no chance of release. In short, there are no second chances. Yet, people's minds take longer to change.

Though 65% of Americans support the death penalty today, ten years ago, the number of people in favor was around 75%. Americans are questioning the death penalty more today as new information surfaces about innocent death row prisoners who have been wrongfully convicted.

David Protess, a professor at Northwestern University, and his journalism class, investigated death penalty cases and uncovered 36 death row prisoners who were innocent.

New evidence surfaced, people came forward with confessions, or police work was flawed. These cases have been in the news and have changed some Americans' minds about the death penalty. The notion of the ultimate revenge is expressed through the death penalty. We have a popular expression in the United States, "Don't get mad, get even." Getting even is what the death penalty does. The murderer killed someone, now we kill the murderer.

Most countries, more than one 100 of the 191 countries recognized by the United Nations, have abolished the death penalty. Compared to other countries, we ranked third in the world in executions after China and Congo. The United States ranked higher than Iran, which was in fourth place. We hear horror stories in the news about killings in Muslim countries of the Middle East, yet when we kill Americans on death row, it is not widely publicized unless the crime was famous. At most, the execution is published as a tiny paragraph in the newspaper. As we criticize other countries' human rights violations, the United States is one of only six countries in the world to execute young people under 18.

Notes

"A jury consists of twelve persons chosen to decide who has the better lawyer."

– Robert Frost, American poet

The American Educational System

 **Elementary School**
5 to 12 years old → Kindergarten to 6th Grade

 **Junior High School**
13 to 14 years old → 7th & 8th Grades (sometimes 9th)

 High School
14 to 18 years old →

9th – 12th Grades
Freshman. 9
Sophomore. 10
Junior 11
Senior. 12

College entrance exam (SAT) score & high school grades must be good.

University / College
Bachelor's degree
4 years, 18 - 22 yrs. old

Community College
Associate's degree
2 - 3 years

Vocational School
Certificate
Weeks to 2 years

 **University**
Master's degree
1 - 2 years

 University
Doctor's degree / Postdoctorate
2 - 6 years specialization

Chapter 9:

Shrinking Teachers & Growing Grades

F oreign business executives and scholars who move their whole family to the United States for a year also enroll their children in American schools. Most are surprised to learn their children are ahead of their American classmates in every subject but English, which shows that our elementary and secondary schools must be lagging behind other countries.

How can Americans win Nobel Prizes for mathematics and science while the majority of us have trouble adding restaurant tips and subtracting our balances in our checkbooks? American twelfth-grade students placed well below the international average in both general math and science knowledge when evaluated against international students from 20 other countries in *The Third International Mathematics and Science Study.* Are we spending too much on research to nurture the brightest students and leaving the rest of us behind?

What are American primary and secondary schools

really like? Education in foreign countries is often divided into public and private schools, with a great difference in the quality of instruction. Since 89% percent of American schools are public and only 11% are private, the United States has both good and bad schools in the public and private sector.

The quality of the education usually depends on whether it is a suburban or inner-city school. The affluent, suburban school with plenty of resources, textbooks, and teachers offers a far better education than the large urban school with scarce resources, overcrowding in the classroom, and buildings with roofs that leak. Suburban schools have swimming pools and well-equipped computer labs. Urban schools have security guards and electronic metal detectors.

Of course, if you are a disciplined student, it doesn't make any difference what school you go to, you'll survive on your own academic initiative. But for a large majority of students attending urban schools, they are only waiting for graduation as they suffer through years of mediocre education.

How schools are funded explains how the dual track educational system was created. The city government collects local property taxes from homeowners and gives a percentage of that money to the schools. Schools also receive grants from the state, which carry many conditions, and finally, schools receive a small amount of money from federal government.

In contrast, students' tuition fees, church subsidies and community fundraisers support private schools. When you send your child to a private school, however, you are still financially supporting the public schools through property taxes.

Most students go to the public school closest to their home. Because real estate properties frequently have lower values in neglected urban neighborhoods, inner city schools receive less money from property taxes. This means that there is less money to spend on students, the maintenance of the school building and even textbooks. Some cities have recently offered a "Choice" program where families can send their child to a school outside their neighborhood. However, families usually have to put their child's name on a long waiting list for another school if they live outside of the area. The time a family must wait to be accepted into another school could be a few months or a few years. Some families also use a relative's address in order to send their child to a better neighborhood school.

As a history teacher in a large inner city school in New York City, the great gap between suburban and urban schools was easily noticeable. The high school, located in a working class neighborhood in Queens, had a population of 3,000 racially-mixed students.

Most teachers did not have enough textbooks to give the students, so copies were made from the teachers' textbook and individual chapters handed out to students. Some teachers had enough textbooks but still did not distribute them because students would not bring them to class or would destroy them.

Indeed, the copy room in the school's basement became a very important place for teachers needing copies.

Teachers paid for their own copies most of the time, since a copy order needed to be filled out two days in advance to get copies from the school.

Some students came to school with weapons, but the teachers didn't want to know who they were. If they knew which students had them, it would make them responsible for reporting them and later face possible retaliation from the student.

Every classroom in this New York City school had a telephone. The telephone had a direct number to the security guards who patrolled the hallways. If you kicked a student out of your class because of bad behavior, you would call a security guard or the dean, who are the people in charge of discipline in high schools. The dean would

School Dress Code

No hats or headgear.

No ripped clothing.

No shirts with obscene sayings.

No baggy pants.

No clothing with a sports team logos.

No shirts with religious symbols.

No sunglasses.

No armbands.

No clothing with drug, alcohol, or tobacco references.

To prevent students with oversized shirts and baggy pants from hiding weapons, many schools have instituted a dress code like the above. Because fights have broken out over designer jackets and athletic shoes in schools, school uniforms are also growing popular in schools.

usually come, take the student out of the class and bring them to his office. Then the student would return to class the next day with the same kind of behavior.

In suburban schools, the school environment may be different. There are usually enough resources, including textbooks, well-equipped computer laboratories, and large recreational facilities. However, discipline and dress code problems exist in suburban schools as well, but perhaps not to the degree of the urban schools.

How do we break this vicious circle? The teachers have very little power today. It's next to impossible to kick out a student with a behavior problem in public schools. The number of students who show up each day determines how much money the school receives from the state and federal government. Teachers, therefore, must record attendance in two separate places to have a permanent record for the school. If a student is kicked out, the school loses money.

For these disruptive students, the duty of teachers is to call the parents and report their behavior. Every teacher has five or six classes and by the end of the day, has a long list of students' names. Teachers spend quite a bit of time calling the students' parents. Many times, family members are not home or do not answer the phone. Still, teachers must record the phone call, which leaves them feeling helpless because of their failure to reach anyone.

Some American parents are not available to punish their children. They are working. Many parents are away most of the day and students are raising themselves. With no one home until evening, misbehaving students are seldom held accountable. The teachers are forced to act like their parents and less like teachers. Meanwhile, for students who really want to learn, it is a frustrating experience because one or two problem students are constantly interrupting classes.

Teachers feel helpless when they want to change the system. They become stressed and tired, or what we call "burned out." Some teachers turn apathetic or hyper-critical of students and the whole school system. A good number of teachers leave and start over in other professions, despite all the benefits and vacation time they will be sacrificing.

Even when most schools have a "zero tolerance" policy of automatically kicking out any student caught possessing weapons or drugs, it's still hard to kick a student out. Schools fear parents will demand equal access to education for their child and if the child is not allowed back, parents may threaten to sue them.

Who controls the schools and sets policies? Since American schools are very decentralized, a group of community leaders called The Board of Education makes the rules for the school. This group of local residents decides the textbooks to be used for the area schools, rules of behavior, and resolves serious problems between a teacher and a student.

In many schools, students cannot wear hats or caps of any kind as they might hide drugs in them. Beepers are not allowed. Every school makes its own policy toward appropriate school dress. Public schools have been recently adopting uniforms for a dress code, a custom usually reserved for private schools. This change has been an effort to reduce gang clothing.

The principal of the school and the Board of Education have most of the power over the school while parents have little control as to what the student learns and many parents feel powerless if they want to change the rules of the school.

Students form little groups in American high schools. This is one institution where you easily see the segregation of races. In the cafeteria or while students are changing classes, you will see the Mexican Americans in one group, the African Americans in another, the Asians with other Asians, and the whites in their separate group. Some students mix with other students outside their group, but it is not very common.

The schools themselves divide students academically

into groups called "tracking" and you follow this academic path throughout your school years. There are Gifted and Talented programs for the very bright kids, Advanced Placement for the college-bound kids, vocational programs for the average kids, and Special Education classes for the slow to learn or students with behavior problems.

Grade inflation is a serious problem in most American schools. Teachers are under tremendous pressure to give high grades whether or not they reflect the student's true academic ability. Many students demand an "A" or a "B" from the teacher these days, and if the grade is anything less, students want to discuss the situation.

For example, if students show up for class, they may get a "C" just for their good attendance. If students do the slightest bit of homework and come to class, they may receive a "B." The full grading scale from "A- F" is seldom used. Teachers rarely fail students for their academic ability because they are under pressure from administrators to pass as many students as they can. If teachers fail students, students may drop out of school and that means less money for the school in the end.

In an effort to combat grade inflation at the college level, Princeton University has instituted a policy in 2004 whereby academic departments will ration the number of As given out to students. Faculty may give A-plus, A or A-minus to no more than 35 percent of the grades given to students, compared to 46 percent of the time in recent years.

Grade inflation can also be seen on the high school level, according to the College Board Report of 2001. The College Board studied American students' SAT scores in 2001 and in 1991. Students with A averages made up 28% of SAT test takers in 1991 compared to 42% in 2001, yet students today have lower SAT test scores than a decade ago. Some high school graduates who have received scholarships because of their grades have even had to take remedial college classes.

Social Cliques

High school students often belong to many social groups. Two of the most common groups are listed below.

Jocks are the athletes. They are usually the most popular students and have status in American high schools.

Nerds are the academic achievers and are seen as not being as socially adept. Nerds often keep a low profile as to their academic ability since being too smart in high school is often seen as not being cool.

Violence

Ten percent of all public schools had violent incidents. Most of the violence is done by students against other students.

Graduating from High School

Exit Exams
Twenty-four of the 50 states have exit exams to pass before you get a high school diploma. Students who do not pass the test may retake it many times.

Community Service
Some states require that students perform volunteer work before they graduate.

"It looks good on the application."
Many American students volunteer in an organization because college admission officials consider these non-academic activities important on a student's application.

Social skills are valued as much as academic abilities in American schools. Academic subjects compete for students' time to participate in team sports, extra-curricular activities, and part-time work after school. Since students are admitted into college based on academics and social development, these activities are taken very seriously.

Which group do you belong to? Peer pressure puts you into groups depending on the balance between academics or sports. *Nerds* are students who study all the time and get good grades. *Jocks* are students on the football or basketball team. As Americans value athletes, the jocks are usually the most popular students in the school. You can be both, of course, a serious student and a member of the basketball team, but there is so much pressure to belong to one group in high school, students usually spend their time with one circle of friends.

The most cheerful, peppy, and energetic people you could ever see are high-school cheerleaders. They try out to become a member of the squad just like a sports team. Dressed in sparkling uniforms and waving pom poms, cheerleaders stand in a line and yell phrases or cheers to encourage their team to win. They also kneel and stand on top of each other like pyramids, do cartwheels and amazing acrobats. Cheerleaders are very entertaining to fans who have come to watch the game.

Compared to Asian countries, where students go to school all day long, American schools look like social centers. After finishing their high school day in the afternoon, many students in Japan and Korea attend tutoring schools and return home to their parents late at night.

The emphasis on sports or other activities in American high schools has led to students graduating with various levels of academic ability. Many high school graduates go to college without the most basic reading and math skills. Colleges, in turn, have been forced to give remedial classes in Math and English. Recently, college officials have pressured high schools to raise their standards by requiring students to take exit exams to get a high school diploma.

Some states have recently adopted the exit exam. High schools, however, are still examining the effect that these exams have on their graduation rates. High school students begin to take the exit exam in tenth grade. The exam consists of an English portion and a math portion. Many students take the math portion of the exam several times before they pass. In the Third International Mathematics and Science Study, a study of U.S. twelfth grade student achievement in math and science in 1998, Americans ranked 19th among math students in 21 countries of the world. The senior year in high school is often dedicated to passing this exit exam. This is in addition to the standardized state tests given every two years throughout school. The number of tests that American students are taking today is dramatically increasing. Some critics believe that this excessive testing in schools is turning our high schools into test preparation institutes rather than schools of learning.

Some American high schools also require students to do community service before they graduate. This requirement is seen as a way to force students to think of others while giving back to the community. Students must work a certain number of hours in activities such as coaching basketball for younger children, reading to the blind, or tutoring elementary-school children. Businesses have also looked for students who have volunteered their time to serve others. Best Buy, an electronics chain, has even offered scholarships for students who do community service. One of their recent ads reads, "We want students with great hearts."

An alternative to either private or public schools is keeping your children home and teaching them yourself. Home schooling is legal in the United States and an estimated one million, or 2%, of children are taught this way. Home-schooled children have school-approved textbooks and guidelines, and a vast network of like-minded parents. Parents who home-school take their children on field trips with other home-schoolers to give their children the social skills that regular schools provide.

Home schooling is on the rise because of the lower academic standards of regular schools. Many parents also choose this option for safety reasons in light of the rise in school shootings. There are other parents who are fundamentalist Christians and choose home schooling because they want to limit their children's exposure to mainstream values.

Getting into College

There is often a big leap from high school to college in the United States. Colleges are much harder, and their academic standards are higher than in high schools. Half of our high school graduates enter college but only 25% graduate. Many drop out because it's too hard, or because it costs too much.

Since the quality of high schools is hard to measure across the nation, we have one standardized admission test, the Scholastic Aptitude Test or SAT, for all colleges in the United States. You must do well on this test to get into college. Many students who get a low score on the SAT go to a community college for two years and later transfer to a four-year university. That way, their grades in the community college are counted instead of the score on the SAT.

The myth in the United States is that all people are treated equally and getting into college is just a question of merit. This is not true. It is not just a matter of what you earned by your good grades and high marks on the various standardized tests, it is more complex than that, and more highly subjective than pure merit.

Besides the SAT score, college admission officials consider the grades you received in high school, an application essay, and your extracurricular activities. Another important factor is if your Mom or Dad went to that college. Sons and daughters of alumni tend to be preferred in the selection process.

On the other hand, if you are the first in your family to go to college, this also makes a difference and weighs in your favor. Some colleges give preference to minorities under a controversial policy called "Affirmative Action."

Colleges in the United States were segregated until the 1950's. The Civil Rights Movement of the 1960's broke down some race barriers and colleges began to recruit blacks and other minorities through their Affirmative Action policies. These policies consider not only grades and activities, but race is also factored into the admission process. Some white students have claimed that they had better grades and qualifications, and yet were not admitted into the college because of the color of their skin. Some "reverse discrimination" cases have been won in court and they have motivated some colleges to eliminate their Affirmative Action policies.

One such case at the University of Michigan recently reached the Supreme Court. The highest court ruled in favor of its Affirmative Action policy. What we may see in the near future is other colleges following suit and reestablishing Affirmative Action programs that they had previously eliminated.

Paying for College

Once American young people get into college, the worry about how to pay for it really begins. Worrying about how to pay for college actually began when you were born, but now payment is required and the immediacy of the need for money sinks in.

Going to college is very expensive for families who are used to having all their public elementary, junior high and high schools free. The average college tuition with room and board for in-state students is $9,000 a year at a four-year public university. For a private four-year university, the average tuition is $28,000, but can be much higher.

Many parents pay for most of their children's college tuition. The rest is usually borrowed from the federal government in the form of student loans that have low-interest rates which vary, but are currently at around 3%. Students apply for any possible financial help. If you are one of the top students, in the top 10% of your high school, you may be able to receive a scholarship that you won't have to pay back.

Most students, however, take out student loans that they must begin paying back to the federal government a year after graduating. Some college students also hold down part-time jobs, but the money earned from a job is usually small and is used for a bit of spending money.

Despite some financial help from the government, American university students usually graduate with nearly $20,000 in debt, and still have to look for their first career-related job in a tight job market. Since finding a job in a field related to your college major is difficult, recent graduates might take any job offer within the first year after graduating. They often do this because of the pressure of having to begin repayment of their student loans. To help students with their college debt, former President Clinton started a national service program called the Americorps, where students can work in a needy neighborhood after college. By working in a public service job or in a low-income neighborhood, recent graduates can cancel all or part of their student loans. This national service program gives an alternative to students.

College Life

Half of the college students in the United States are adults 25 and over. It's not unusual to see someone your mother's age, or even your grandmother's age, sitting next to you in the college classroom and asking what the homework was from the last class. Many are working adults with families who have decided to go back to school for professional advancement. Others never finished college, but have decided to return several years later.

Many of our colleges have international students advancing their careers in their countries with an American graduate degree. While only 2% of the student body is international for undergraduate programs, at the graduate level, international students make up 20% of our master's programs and 30% of our doctoral degrees. Business is the most popular field of study for international students in the United States, followed by engineering, math, and computer science.

People from other countries are surprised to learn that American college students often change their majors in the course of their college years. Some students do not know what their major field of study will be, even though they are in their first or second year of college. College students can register their major as "undeclared," and still take classes in many subjects. When asked what they will do with their degree after graduating from college, a great number of college students say they do not know beyond "look for a job."

Fraternities and Sororities

On American college campuses, the land of alleged equality, we have peculiar social clubs that cost a lot of money to join, called fraternities and sororities. Fraternities are exclusive all male clubs, and sororities are all female clubs. They are more than just clubs, however, these groups rent houses and live together and do most of their social activities together. You can see their presence in the Greek letters that identify these groups such as *Sigma Alpha Epsilon* and *Alpha Delta Phi*.

At the beginning of each semester or quarter,

fraternities and sororities recruit new members through a process called rush week. They host a series of parties at the houses where they invite potential club members to get to know the current members.

The purpose of these clubs is to meet somebody of your own social class, namely, upper middle class or upper class, instead of possibly choosing your life partner from a much bigger social circle. Exclusivity is the key issue here because these clubs have annual dues that students must pay. Fraternities and sororities also charge students a membership fee, which could be from hundreds to thousands of dollars a year to join, depending on the fraternity or sorority you choose.

These clubs are well-known for their beer-drinking parties. They order kegs, turn the music up loud, and often party inside and outside of their fraternity or sorority houses. They are a very noticeable presence on college campuses, and in the surrounding neighborhoods if they live off-campus. They tend to be the noisiest houses on the block. Some of these houses have caused enough problems that neighbors have complained and colleges have put restrictions on them. Some fraternities and sororities have even been banned entirely from college campuses.

In addition to the sorority and fraternity clubs found on American college campuses, sports take on a new importance in college. Sports teams bring in money, and athletes are often recruited for their ability on the field, not in the classroom. Many adults watch college sports on television and the teams are big moneymakers for the university. This may be why universities have made academic exceptions for athletes. Alumni, or former graduates of a university, are big contributors to colleges when they have a winning football team. This, in turn, allows colleges to offer athletes a generous "benefits package" and sends a message to young adults that athletes are highly valued in our society.

American houses are bigger but our families are smaller...

2000

2200 square feet
(204 square meters)
Family size: 2.6

1970

1,500 square feet
(139 square meters)
Family size: 3

1950

1,000 square feet
(93 square meters)
Family size: 3.4

Source: U.S. Census Bureau & National Association of Home Builders

Chapter 10:

A House for Display

V isitors to the United States are often surprised to see that American houses are often single family detached homes. Our housing developed this way with a population density so low that we could afford the space. There are 70 people per square mile (29 people per square kilometer) compared to Japan's density of 880 people per square mile (340 people per square kilometer), reports the United Nations in 2001.

Many multi-levels houses or apartments in urban areas of the United States are known as "projects" rather than high-rises because they are often reserved for low-income families who receive government assistance. Public housing is usually located in the downtown areas of cities, and it suffers from a bad reputation as a place of criminal activity.

Other foreign visitors comment on how plain our houses are. Unlike Europe, we live in homes with few architectural details or ornamentation, especially if built after World War II. Few cathedrals exist in the United States, and the only castle is in Disneyland.

Most American homes are single-family detached houses and cheaply built. We commonly use wood because we used to have abundant forests that provided us with lumber. Even if it's a highly flammable building material compared to brick, stone or concrete, wood is still used because it is inexpensive. For the West Coast, wood is also a lighter construction material in the case of an earthquake.

The East Coast and Midwest regions have sturdier houses made of brick, stone and concrete and often have a basement for the tornadoes or hurricanes possible in those areas. Building materials also need to be stronger and more insulated for the colder climates.

The Southwest has little rain so we see flat-roofed houses. Unlike countries in Latin America with similar climates, Americans do not make the roof of the house sturdy enough to use as a patio. We would need to invest in cement frames and posts, which would mean more expensive materials. That kind of cement construction in the United States is generally reserved for public buildings.

Today, new American homes have walls and floors made of drywall and plywood about an inch (25 cm) thick. If you live in an apartment complex, the sounds of your neighbors travel through the walls and make for little privacy. You hear neighbors' footsteps and flushing toilets, too.

It's a bit unusual that Americans love privacy, but their homes usually have a huge window facing the street in order to view the world from the inside. People passing by on the street can also peer in from the outside and see what is going on inside the house. Americans like privacy, but that implies privacy in the family. The sense of privacy among strangers isn't as strong.

Most American houses are not fenced or gated so the home's entrance is not protected at all. In some neighborhoods, the front door of the house is only steps away from the street. Compared to other countries that have heavily gated entrances, such as Brazil, it seems most Americans blindly trust that burglars won't break into their homes, or gangs won't ruin the exterior of their homes.

Our nation is a little more than 200 years old, and therefore American houses are often built to conform to housing styles from Europe. We use every period time imaginable; Victorian, Queen Anne's, or Tudor just to name a few.

Today, new houses are built like Hollywood movie sets. Real estate developers plan communities with identical houses and a certain time period and style. The wooden frame is put up practically overnight. A facade of plaster an inch thick covers the thin walls and now you have a cheap replica of a 15th century Mediterranean, or you can go back to the Middle Ages with a Tudor style, imitate a Spanish mission, or a Western ranch.

Who cares if there are no palm trees naturally growing in your region of the country? If you want to project a tropical paradise, a retail store of exotic plants is around the corner. Palm trees can be imported from thousands of miles away and planted to give your property an authentic twist.

Sixty-seven percent of Americans own their homes. We have mobile homes that provide an affordable home to many people who otherwise wouldn't be able to own a home. These houses on wheels are the modern-day equivalent of covered wagons. Owners of the mobile homes usually take off the wheels and park their homes in a rented space in a mobile park. Mobile parks operate like a regular neighborhood, though major storms and tornadoes have been known to sweep through and destroy entire mobile home parks in the United States.

Americans feel nostalgic for their rural roots. The frontier has remained with us. The vast open spaces of the prairie can be seen in the front and back of American homes. Today, they are called front and back yards. They are mowed and trimmed just to sit there like "Little Houses on the Prairie."

Garages

There are 65 million garages in the U.S. and demand for bigger ones is growing.

Three-car Garages

18% of American homes have three-car garages, but only 13% of Americans parked three cars in their garages.

Using Garages For Storage

We fill them with wheelbarrows, camping gear, bicycles, a workbench, another refrigerator, a lawn mower and gardening tools.

Front and Back Yards

Having nicely mowed lawns is a symbol of status among neighbors in the United States. The lawn tradition was transplanted to the United States from England.

○ **Front Yards** – During most of the year, the front yard must be finely trimmed with edges clearly cut. In the winter, how you decorate your house for the holidays is also a sign of status when lawns can no longer be displayed.

○ **Back Yards** – Back yards (and sometimes front yards) are sometimes filled with play structures for kids, a pool, a deck and a grill for barbecues in the summer.

○ *"Not in my backyard,"* is an American expression for anywhere but here. When communities want to open a drug rehabilitation, recycling center or low-income housing, sometimes neighbors organize and protest having these places in their neighborhood.

Few Americans plant vegetable and flower gardens, but instead, carefully maintain their lawns. To an outsider, these unused lawns seem to be a waste of space. But to an American, they fulfill the longing for open space and the feeling of "being free." Unused spaces seem to contradict the notion that Americans are practical people. These ideas of space may be on an unconscious level to most Americans. When asked about their expansive lawns, many just want to have a piece of land so others can admire it.

While houses have grown larger in the suburbs, families have shrunk. The average size home in the United States is 2,200 square feet (204 square meters), according to the National Association of Home Builders, in its *Housing Facts, Figures and Trends 2004* report. In 1970, the average new single home being built was 1,500 square feet (139 square meters). At the same time, the average family has gone from an average of two or three children a generation ago to couples having one or two children with many families remaining childless.

We have so much space that we don't even realize it. To put our roominess in perspective, compare the square meters or footage to a sampling of countries around the world, based on Peter Menzel's book, *Material World*.

In Japan, the average size house, 1421 sq. ft. (132 square meters). Size of household: 4 people. Living room, dining room, kitchen, and bath. Traditionally, Japan has used one room for many purposes: to eat meals, socialize and to sleep. After meals, the dining table was put away and then mats were laid down to sleep on the floor. Today, many young Japanese have the Western style of bed, which is often put in the corner of the multi-purpose room similar to a studio apartment here in the United States.

In Brazil, the average size house is 1,100 sq. feet. (102 square meters). Size of household: 6 people. Two bedrooms, living room, kitchen, bathroom.

In Italy, 1292 sq. ft. (120 sq. meters). Size of household: 3 people. Five rooms and a garage.

In China, 600 square feet (55 square meters). Size of household: 9 people. Kitchen, living room, 3 bedrooms, 5 storage rooms.

Why do Americans want such a big home? Many Americans subconsciously view their house as a museum. They buy a big home, decorate it with expensive furniture, plaster their walls with family photos, and sometimes fill their house up with one or two children. They are busy working to pay the mortgage on this monster of a house. They only live in the house a handful of hours on Saturday and Sunday, besides sleeping there, of course.

While many Americans love a big kitchen, not that many of us cook in it. It's on exhibit too. We put in all new wooden cabinets to match the counter, stainless steel sinks, a built-in microwave and we wait for the day people come in and admire it and compliment the owners on a job well done.

Inside the house, it is common for the living room and the bedrooms not to have an overhead light fixture. You must buy lamps to light up your rooms. The dim lights of a lamp might seem like cozy candlelight compared to the bright florescent lights of Korean and Japanese homes.

A typical American house has an ice maker built into the refrigerator, a garbage disposal in the sink, air conditioners that are often set at frostbite temperatures, central heating that can be set so high as to interfere with normal breathing, and a basement that is seldom used. Opening windows is becoming rare, as we prefer the artificial air. Indoor carpeting is common in living rooms and bedrooms, and we seldom take off our shoes when entering our homes. Americans who buy white carpets, status symbols in the United States, may have the rule of taking off their shoes, but this is strictly for practical reasons.

Allergies are a fairly common ailment in the United States and some people claim that it is due to the strong custom of having carpeting, which collects dust, along with the habit of using artificial air in our houses.

The refrigerator, in particular, has taken on a strange role in American culture. This oversized box not only stores our food but also serves as a family communication center.

Used as a bulletin board, it is decorated with photos, children's artwork, grocery lists, messages, memos, calendars and just about anything else to remind us how proud or how busy we are as a family.

Many international students refuse to dry their clothes in American dryers. They claim that these machines are so powerful they can turn clothes into garments with loose threads or a size smaller. Hanging our clothes to drip dry in the bathroom may take quite a while to dry, but it is an option to putting clothes in the dryer, as few people in the United States use clotheslines.

Americans are reluctant to hang laundry out the window, backyard, or patio as in other countries. This could be because Americans like the convenience of having a dryer. Yet we have garage sales. Once or twice a year we empty our cluttered houses and spread our clothes out on the front yard. Aren't we ashamed of showing our personal belongings to the neighbors and asking them to buy our junk? No, the notion of making money off our belongings seems to outweigh any embarrassment for this weekend event.

Another American paradox is that we often worry about saving money in our own home and yet freely spend on the home, too. We turn off the lights to save on the electric bill. We turn down the temperature of our water heaters and take short showers so the water bill is low. At the same time, we set a timer to water the grass every day. The sprinkler waters the grass even if it has rained on a particular day. In warm weather, we turn on the air conditioner to frigid temperatures.

For the Japanese and some European visitors, the bathrooms of the United States seem impractical. We have the bathtub, toilet, and sink all in the same room while in Japan, these rooms are all separate, so one person can use the sink or the toilet while another person is in the bathtub.

The majority of Americans take a quick shower before work. This daily ritual is seen as a means to get clean in the quickest way possible, which is unlike the ritual in Japan, where a bath is seen as a place to take your time and relax, and bathing even has a spiritual side. Americans seldom take time to relax this way, as bathing is not often viewed as a spiritual experience.

When Americans invite friends over, they clean the house and get it ready to be displayed. It is a major occasion. The house will be on exhibit. When the guests arrive, we show them around the house, (the viewing), and endlessly talk about our remodeling projects (exhibit in progress). Americans expect visitors to compliment them on the furnishings of the house or something hanging on their walls (the reception).

At the same time we have made our houses into museums, American art and science museums offer children the opportunity to stay overnight at the museum. American parents are willing to pay top dollar for their children to be educated in a museum while enjoying an overnighter with other children. The irony is found in a culture where houses are museums and museums are houses.

This notion of improving the house that you just bought is an American trait. Why aren't we satisfied with what we just bought? We always think change is better; we can always improve our house and ourselves.

Even when we have money to hire outside contractors, many of us will remodel our own homes ourselves. We go to the giant furniture and hardware stores full of prefabricated and packaged walls, windows, cabinets, lights, and furniture. By following the instructions included in the package, we assemble cabinets and install bathroom fixtures with minimal skills and tools.

This trend for remodeling your home is very popular abroad too. In the United States, we have Martha Stewart, the home decorating guru, to help us. Though Martha

Stewart was found guilty of lying about a stock-trading deal and was sentenced to five months in prison in July of 2004, Stewart plans to continue giving out recipes and entertaining ideas to her American followers. While we have Martha Stewart to tell us how to decorate our interior in the United States, in other countries, they have their own queens of interior design helping them remake their homes.

Few Americans give a thought to what their neighbors do. Homes are left empty for most of the day while Americans are working, so most of us don't have a chance to know our neighbors. Usually we know their names and where they work. Neighbors also move in and out frequently so we don't invest much of our time in getting to know them well.

Most Americans think the perfect neighbors are the ones who are quiet and mind their own business. Dogs barking, music played too loud, and domestic abuse are common problems in the neighborhood. Neighbors often call the police and report the neighbor if something bothers them or if they hear a physical fight in the house next door.

Why do Americans call the police to solve their problems instead of telling the neighbor face to face or calling them on the phone? If we report a neighbor to the police, we can usually remain anonymous and feel safer than by revealing our name. What will the angry neighbor do in retaliation? The neighbor usually finds out, however, not because the police told them but because they know their neighbors well enough to figure out who reported them. Usually nothing happens, but the neighbor probably stops talking to you and begins to regard you as an enemy.

The Homeless

First-time visitors to the United States are amazed at the number of homeless we have in this country. This reflects that the gap between the rich and the poor is getting wider in this country.

In the United States, men without jobs hold up a sign instead of extending their hand. They stand on a corner all day with a piece of cardboard, and on it is usually written, "Homeless, please help," or "Will work for food." They beg during daylight, and some return to a house at night. Some of these homeless are not homeless at all, but they are jobless. Others, however, are truly homeless, and rummage through garbage dumpsters for cans and bottles at night or in early morning hours.

Those who are truly homeless and sleeping on the streets can be identified by their tattered clothes, blankets, and shopping cart full of discards. We do have shelters for them in our large cities, but not nearly enough. The shelters have curfews and rules about alcohol and drugs. Many of the homeless have addiction problems that forbid them to use the shelters.

It's fairly easy to become homeless in this country. We have a saying that many of us are "one step away from being homeless." If you lose your job, there isn't much of a support system from your family and friends. You usually receive six months of unemployment income from the government. Our welfare system mainly qualifies you for assistance if you have children, which of course, means mothers. You see more single, middle-aged men who are homeless on the street because they make up the majority of homeless in the United States, according to the *Interaging Council on the Homeless* 1999 report. Many women and children are homeless too, but often live in homeless shelters.

Notes

"A man builds a house in England with the expectation of living in it and leaving it to his children; we shed our houses in America as easily as a snail does his shell."

– Harriet Beecher Stowe, American author (1811-1896)

Diverse Religions

The Mormons *(also known as The Latter-day Saints)*

○ Nine million members in more than 150 countries and territories. About 4.5 million live in the U.S.

○ Founder Joseph Smith, religious book: *The Book of Mormon.*

○ **Live a disciplined life** – No coffee, tea, cigarettes, alcohol or premarital sex.

○ **Baptism of the dead** – Because of the belief of baptism of their ancestors, the tracing of one's family tree has become very important to the Mormons. This religion holds one of the best genealogical archives in the U.S.

○ **Two-year missionary service** – For single young men (19 years old) or retired couples. They travel in pairs. One and a half year missionary assignment for single females (21 years old).

The Christian Scientists *(The Church of Christ)*

○ 200,000 members, based in Boston, Mass.

○ Founder Mary Baker Eddy, 1879, religious text: *Science and Health.*

○ **Refuse medical treatment** and rely on faith healing by Christian Science practitioners. Claims of miraculous healing.

The Amish *(also known as "The Plain People")*

○ 144,000 members, founder Jacob Amman.

○ Emigrated from Europe as farmers in the 1700s and 1800s, mainly live in the rural Midwest today.

○ **Reject modern conveniences** such as electricity, cars, air travel, jewelry and divorce.

○ **Amish families have an average of seven children**. Almost 25% have ten or more children.

○ **Follow *Ordnung* rules**: Wear dark clothing, marry other Amish, and will not serve in the military.

Chapter 11:

God & Good Luck

W hy are people so religious in the United States? We talk about God all the time in our political and legal institutions. The president ends his political speeches with, *"God bless America."* The U.S. Congress starts with a prayer before it begins its session. American children stand up at the beginning of their school day reciting "The Pledge of Allegiance" while promising to be loyal to *". . . one nation, under God."* Our coins say, *"In God we trust."* If you are a witness in a trial, you take an oath: "Do you swear to tell the whole truth and nothing but the truth, *so help you God?"*

Is this the same country that proclaims the separation of church and state? What you see are many references to God because the overwhelming majority believe in a God. In a recent Harris Poll, Americans were surveyed about their religious beliefs and 90% of Americans said they believed in God, but *less than half* of the population actually practice religious rituals by going to a church on a regular basis.

While Americans have limited choice for presidential and congressional candidates, with only two major political parties, the number of religious groups is extensive. Protestants alone count over 300 denominations, according to to Barry A. Kosmin and Seymour P. Lachman in *One Nation Under God*, a book that presents the results of an extensive 1990 national survey in which 100,000 Americans were asked to identify their religion.

Who are the religious in America?

Fifty-two percent of American adults are Protestant, 24.5% are Catholic and 14.1% adhere to no religion, reports *The American Religious Identification Survey 2001*, an in-depth survey asking Americans about their religion. This 2001 survey was done by City University of New York as a follow-up to the extensive *One Nation Under God* 1990 survey.

As you can see, about 77% of Americans claim Christianity as their religion. Christianity is on the decline, however, in the United States. The 2001 survey revealed the number of Americans who claim to be Christians went from 86% only ten years ago to the current 77%. Over the same ten-year period, Americans who were not affiliated with any religion jumped from 8% to 14%.

Still, Christianity continues to dominate the fabric of our society. Religious diversity in the United States is Christian diversity. Considering our ethnic diversity, a surprising number of people in this country have a similar outlook about religion.

Americans ranked first in a 1989 Gallup International survey asking young adults 18 to 24 the importance of religion. Ninety percent of American young adults said it was important, compared to young Brazilians (80%), Koreans (68%), Japanese (38%) and Chinese (4%).

While most Americans agree on the basic Christian beliefs, they vary widely on the organized practice of their religion.

On one hand, you have people who attend Church on

an occasional basis, for baptisms, funerals and at Christmas and Easter. Their Bible probably is collecting dust on the bedroom nightstand. These are Christians who don't participate in the organized part of religion and see their faith as a largely private matter between God and themselves.

On the other hand, you have the fundamentalists and evangelical Christians, most heavily in the Southern states, who make up the 20% of Christians who are considered extremely religious. They are the "born again" Christians who are on a mission to convert the rest of the world to Christianity. Many of these fundamentalists are ardent churchgoers who go to church more than once a week, read their Bible on a daily basis and interpret the Bible literally. They don't smoke, drink, or dance. Southern Baptists are by far the largest majority of fundamentalists in the United States, making up one third of the Protestants.

This religious divide between those who pay lip service to their Church versus the active, practicing Christians in the United States polarizes Americans more than the differences between Catholics and Protestants.

Some active church members give to churches because this donation is tax deductible. This can reduce the amount of money Americans pay to the state and federal government at tax time. If there is one thing Americans hate it is paying taxes. A popular adage in the United States says, "There are only two things you must do in the United States, die and pay taxes."

Most Americans think Christianity is exclusive. You can't believe in Christianity and another religion at the same time. This concept differs in other countries, where they borrow religious rites and believe that different religions can be practiced alongside one another.

In Japan, for example, people practice rituals from different religions at different stages of their life. When a baby is born, the Japanese go to a shrine to pray to the native gods. At certain ages 3,5 and 7, the Japanese also go a shrine to celebrate their children's birthdays in the Shinto style. In a wedding ceremony, many go to a church and exchange marriage vows in front of Christ. Then it is a common Japanese practice to bury the dead in a Buddhist ceremony. This type of practicing various religious rites at different times in your life is unheard of in the United States.

Many immigrants change their religion when they come to the United States. Those who were not religious in their native countries arrive here and may join a religion out of sheer loneliness and the overwhelming feeling of being an outsider to the mainstream culture.

When Korean immigrants come to the United States, many of them join a Christian church, though Koreans have traditionally come from a Buddhist country. Korean immigrants often become active in churches here to feel a part of a community that often substitutes for the family unit they miss in their countries. Some have changed because of the social aspects of Christianity compared to Buddhism's more personal view. Also, there are few Buddhists temples in the United States.

Hispanic immigrants often change their religion in the United States too. Latin America is predominantly Catholic, but in the United States, Hispanics who become Protestants tend to gravitate toward the Evangelicals and Pentecostals. The Protestant faiths recruit new members with strong missionary activities compared to the Catholic denomination. They also offer social services and access to government services, which the Catholics also offer, but to a lesser degree. Some of these Protestant churches even sponsor the newly-arrived immigrants. If immigrants work three years as religious workers for the church, the church may help them get their permanent legal residence.

Some churches cater to the new immigrant and are called ethnic churches. They offer English language classes, job and housing assistance as well as serving immigrants' spiritual needs.

The government typically provides these kinds of

services to Americans. In the case of immigrants, however, it is frequently the church that helps them to adjust to a new life in the United States. Moreover, the church gives them practical information and a social network of people who speak their own language.

Religion in the United States is less based on ethnic history, like Hinduism, Buddhism, and Muslim faiths, and more based on personal choice. Americans choose their denomination in the Christian faith and see nothing wrong with changing churches. You can go to a Methodist church service this Sunday and then a Lutheran service the next. You can officially change from Catholic to Pentecostal if you want to take some classes.

Americans may believe in many things that their organized religion might not follow. They see nothing wrong with this. For example, the Catholic Church is against abortion and divorce, but many Catholics believe these are personal issues and disagree with Church teaching. On the issue of abortion, Americans who believe in the right to have an abortion are not called supporters of abortion but *pro choice.*

How old you are may also determine your church attendance. American children usually follow their parents to church, as the parents want to pass on the moral principles of their religion to their children. This church attendance may drop off during the teen years. As adults age, attendance at religious services rises again. Seniors make up a large number of the faithful in churches. Could this reflect the fact that many seniors live alone, and may be one of the loneliest groups of people in American society?

Going to Catholic churches in the United States differs from the churches in other Catholic countries. In Latin American countries, the Catholic Church usually is very ornate and people come to pray silently and intensely for loved ones, often clutching a photograph or rosary.

Here, going to Church is very informal. Some people wear jeans, come to Mass late, and bring crayons and coloring books to keep their child occupied for an hour. All of this makes the religious ritual resemble more of a social gathering than a religious ceremony.

We shake hands with the usher when we go into church. Then during the Mass, we offer each other the sign of peace, shaking hands with people around us and wishing them peace. We recite the Lord's Prayer, holding hands with the person in our pew. We clap at the end of Mass to show the appreciation to the organist who plays the music.

As we go out the door, we greet the priest at the bottom of the steps where he waits to shake hands with us, and we thank him for the sermon. After mass, most people meet in the church hall for coffee and doughnuts to socialize some more. In the United States, with three handshakes and one round of applause, the mass is less a spiritual ritual than a "feel happy" pageant where people are the performers.

Christianity is so strong in the United States that the Muslims, Jews, Buddhists, and Hindus take a back seat in the religious spectrum. Americans have varying degrees of tolerance for other religions. In the past, we had freedom of religion as long as it was our religion. Native Americans were practicing their own tribal religions when the colonists arrived. Then these unknown and frightening religions were forbidden. Native Americans were not allowed to practice their religious ceremonies and publicly pray to their gods again until 1978, when the federal government passed the American Indian Religious Freedom Act.

Black slaves had their African tribal religions when they arrived, but were forced to convert to Christianity. This forced conversion worked against the white man in the long run. It indirectly helped eliminate slavery, as religion became a spiritual fountain for slaves hoping for freedom. Churches also turned out to be the places to politically organize against the white man in the segregated South.

When Americans see Muslim women covered with a headscarf or Jewish men with a cap, we tend to feel uncomfortable. If two Christians are carrying around a Bible, however, few Americans are surprised. We are accustomed to seeing missionaries on street corners. Still, when any religious minority shows something public, such as dressing in religious garb, it makes many Americans nervous because of a belief that religion should be private, not public.

Americans tend to overestimate the size of minority religions in the United States, which account for only 4% of the population. The most visible minority religions are from the Jewish and Muslim faiths. Though Jews make up only 1.3% of our religious population and Muslims 0.5%, their religious dress and holidays often identify these religious minorities and makes them a target of prejudice.

New York is the home to more Jews (25%) and Muslims (24%) than any other state. In New York City, for example, public schools have the major Jewish holidays off. In schools throughout the United States, however, school officials have been challenged to accommodate religious minorities. This means schools have had to excuse students' absences for religious holidays or find a place for Muslim students to go to at lunchtime during the month of Ramadan, when Muslim students fast.

The term Arab is an ethnic category, and Islam is a religion. Not all Arabs are Muslims and not all Muslims are Arabs. Most Americans confuse Arabs with Muslims and think they are the same. This is a myth based on the lack of knowledge of cultures other than our own.

In fact, the majority of Arabs in the United States are not Muslims. Arab Christians such as Egyptian Copts, Lebanese Maronites and Iraqi Chaldeans have made their home here.

The Muslim faith is growing fast in the United States because of the large numbers of African Americans who convert to Islam today.

We have had anti-Catholic incidents in the past, but today anti-Semitic and anti-Muslim sentiments prevail with a rise in hate crimes directed toward Jews and Muslims. In the year 2002, the FBI reported 1,039 hate crimes against Jews and 170 against Muslims in its Uniform Crime Reports.

Secular groups, the 14% who don't claim any religion, include humanists, secularists, and atheists. They have been instrumental in keeping Christian practices out of schools.

Madalyn Murray, a Texas atheist, challenged Bible reading and prayers in public schools. She fought against a 1963 mandatory Bible reading law in Pennsylvania schools, and the case reached the Supreme Court. She also challenged saying the "Our Father" prayer in Maryland public schools.   The Supreme Court ruled on these cases together and banned government-sponsored religious activities in public schools since.

Other battles are still being fought in the courts to keep religion out of schools and courthouses. In 2003, after two years of controversy and $1 million dollars in lawyer's fees, the Alabama Courthouse had to remove a monument that was inscribed with the Ten Commandments.

The fight between religion and state continues around the world. In France, a law was recently enacted which bans head scarves for Muslim girls, skullcaps for Jewish boys and large crosses for Christians.

Good Luck

When Americans cannot figure out why something happened, which they constantly try to do, they resort to talking about good luck and bad luck. Luck is more socially acceptable to talk about than beliefs in God, though we talk about both.

Some of us become jealous when we see other people doing well. We dismiss the success of others and say, "They were lucky." Or if something bad happens to people who we think did not deserve the misfortune, we say the opposite, " It was a case of bad luck."

If we interpret success and misfortune in religious terms, it would sound something like this for misfortune, "It was meant to be," or for success, "My prayers were answered." You hear these expressions in the United States, too. By observing what Americans say when told of good and bad news, you can often gauge how religious they are.

Good luck in the United States is a very general, catch-all term to wish someone well in whatever he undertakes. In fact, it is a common way of saying good-bye when we know a person has to take a test, apply for a job, or get out of a troublesome predicament.

I *lucked out* means I was lucky. The luck of the Irish means you were very lucky, though you don't have to be Irish to claim this special status. Many Americans wear a special piece of jewelry for luck, and wearing good luck charms is as common as seeing Christian crosses. You can spot these good luck charms hanging from the rear view window of many cars. There is even a popular cold cereal called Lucky Charms.

In some countries, people don't use the words good luck as often as we do. In the Korean language, words for wishing good luck are usually tied to a particular event. For example, when you take a test, there is a special word to do well on the test that would be equivalent to the American general "good luck." When a baby is born, there is another kind of good luck word. For ritual moments and everyday situations, the word changes and is tied to the action. In English, our vocabulary isn't as rich to express the nuances of the event. The most you could do to tie it to an event is say, "Good luck on your test."

Americans knock on wood three times when they say good things about themselves. This is to prevent bad things from happening by telling others of our successes. This practice dates back to pre-Christian times when we believed trees had good and bad spirits inside. By knocking on them, the evil spirits would be driven away.

Some Americans also believe in astrology and may ask you, "What's your sign?" The Western horoscope is based on your birthday and divided into 12 astrological signs with a whole set of personality characteristics for each sign. Some people believe that if you know the hour and the exact date you were born, a person shares personality traits with other people born with similar planetary experiences.

"Are you Aquarius? You must be friendly. Libras and Aquarians get along." While some Americans just follow astrology for fun, others really believe in it as a kind of prediction.

Americans rarely know our blood type unless we have had a medical problem and our doctors have told us. This often surprises international people, especially the Japanese. The Japanese not only ask each other about their blood types, but some even want to match the compatibility of their blood type to a potential mate.

In Chinese and Korean cultures, people often go to a fortune teller to determine the best date on the calendar to get married. Americans do not have this idea that certain days are considered lucky days to get married or to make major business decisions. The closest equivalent would be the daily horoscope column in newspapers.

Good luck and bad luck numbers vary in cultures, too. In China, the numbers 6 and 8 are considered good luck numbers. In Chinese, 6 means smoothly and 8 means fortune. If you put 6 and 8 together, it roughly means good fortune.

We consider the number 13 as unlucky in the United States, as do many Western European and Latin American countries. Skyscrapers are built without the 13th floor. However, the number 4 is considered unlucky in Japan, Korea and China because the pronunciation of this word sounds similar to the word "death." Many people in these countries do not want cell phone numbers with the number 4 in them.

Notes

"We are all tattooed in our cradles with the beliefs of our tribe."

– Oliver Wendell Holmes, Sr.
American author and physician (1809-1904)

Cities That Restrict Cars to Reduce Traffic

Rome, Florence and Milan
These Italian cities have closed the center of their cities to cars, making them wonderful walking cities.

Mexico City
This city has closed the downtown Zocalo area to automobiles.

London
Drivers must pay to enter the center of the city.

Hong Kong
Drivers must pay to enter the city.

Singapore
Drivers of cars with fewer than four people pay a monthly fee if they enter the city during the morning rush hour.

Tokyo
Car owners must show government officials that they have rented a parking space or car port before they are able to register their cars.

Chapter 12:

A Colony of Cars

W hat do Americans do in cars? Roll down your window and take a look. We put on make-up, undress and dress ourselves, drink hot coffee, pick our nose, read the newspaper and work from our cell phones. We seem to think because a metal bubble encases us, our private life is invisible.

We even party in parking lots, which we call a "tailgate party." Before a football game, we open our trunks packed with beer and sandwiches, unfold chairs and sit in the parking lot with friends to get in the mood to see a football game.

Our cars talk. What we wish to stand up for and say in person, we stick on our cars. Bumper stickers and license plate frames reveal our deepest feelings and political beliefs. There must be a great number of proud parents in this country because one of the most common bumper stickers is, "My child is an honor student at Jefferson Elementary School." The second most common sticker is when that child is all grown up and now shows off what college he graduated from by displaying a sticker that says, "Alumni of New York University."

Then there are the bumper stickers that tell us where we would like to be, "I'd rather be shopping." Others show how much we love our cats and dogs, how sexy we are, and what non-profit organizations we are members of.

The car is so much a part of the American psyche that a driver's license functions as a national identity card in the United States. "Carding you" is another way to ask for our identification when we buy alcohol or cigarettes. Everyone is supposed to have one. Even if you don't drive, you get the same card as a driver. The only difference is that the card is used for identity purposes instead of driving. Police officers, of course, use your driver's license number when they stop you for traffic violations. By entering your number, they can access all kinds of personal information on the computer installed in the police car. Besides the ownership and registration of the car, your driving record and previous home addresses can be accessed in minutes.

Some Americans who can't afford a house invest in a beautiful car instead. It is a status symbol. They install stereo equipment and CD players in their BMWs or convertibles and cruise around with the volume turned up and the sound of the car vibrates for blocks.

Americans feel more powerful in their cars. When we get mad at a driver in heavy traffic, we are ruder and more aggressive than if we were face to face. This aggressive behavior is called "road rage." We hang our heads out of the window or get close enough to the other car so we can curse at them. A few people even try to side-swipe your car. Other people get out of their cars in heavy traffic or at a stoplight and start yelling at a driver who had failed to use turn signals or had cut in front of a car.

Though the Toyota Camry and the Honda Civic have been competing for the best-selling car title in the last couple of decades, many of us prefer to drive big cars like

Sport Utility Vehicles, commonly known as SUVs.

Why do we drive so many big cars and trucks? We feel like kings of the road. We like to see above other cars and we want the comfort of the space, since we spend an enormous amount of time in our cars. Americans drive an average of two hours a day just going back and forth to work. This does not include the time spent in our cars doing errands and dropping off and picking up our children. We live in our cars.

Do Americans even consider gas mileage? For many people, the power and comfort that comes with space is considered more important than the mileage and the cost of gasoline. As long as gas is cheaper than most of the world pays, we'll keep buying SUVs and other gas-guzzlers.

Cars have made walking around in the city mostly obsolete in the United States. Most Americans dislike walking as a means for transport. In Europe, people make between 25-40% percent of their trips by foot or bicycle in suburbs, compared to just 7 percent of Americans' trips. Walking is seen as a hardship or a sign of poverty. It is only socially acceptable when it looks like an organized sport and it looks sweaty. Proper exercise shorts, a sleeveless T-shirt, a Walkman, and sports shoes are needed. A fast, hard stride makes us look like serious walkers. In the United States, we like to say, "I took a *power walk.*" With our arms swinging back and forth and our feet pounding the cement, we look straight ahead and count how many blocks we've walked and how many calories we are burning off.

Our refusal to see walking as a pleasurable means of getting somewhere even applies to short trips around the neighborhood. Why should we walk when we have driveways next to our houses? Many Americans even drive a short walking distance to places in our neighborhoods such as banks, the dry cleaners and the post office. The convenience of having drive-through fast food restaurants,

Cities Noted for Car Alternatives

○ **Curitiba, Brazil** – Has a unique bus system. Buses run on dedicated streets and provide excellent, low-cost service.

○ **Basel, Switzerland** – This city is heavily dependent on an excellent tram system and parts of the town are car-free.

○ **Groningen, Netherlands** – This European city promotes bikes as a practical means of transportation. The Netherlands also leads the world in the number of bicycle paths.

○ **Tokyo, Japan** – Fast trains replace cars in most of Tokyo.

Europe's Most Dangerous Drivers
Although Italy has a reputation for bad drivers, the worst drivers were surprisingly found in the UK in a five-country survey.

The countries polled in the International Road Traffic and Accident survey were: the UK, Germany, Italy, Spain and France.

banks and camera shops in neighborhoods discourages walking, too.

The dislike for walking can also be seen in these parking lots, where people can be quite aggressive over a parking spot. Many Americans will drive around and around a parking lot for several minutes in order to find the closest space possible so they don't have to walk so far. For people who are willing to pay for valet parking, parking attendants will help us out of our cars and leave us at the entrance of a shopping mall or fine restaurant.

Many Americans also choose not to walk to their destinations because streets in the United States are strictly made for the car. A great number of our roads lack marked crosswalks, pedestrian signals or bridges in order for people to cross a busy street. Streets without sidewalks force people to walk along the side of the road with high-speed traffic. In many states, it is legal to make a right turn on a red light after stopping in an intersection. This practice can cause accidents with pedestrians crossing the street.

Bicycling in the United States is not as popular as in Europe either. People of all ages bike in Europe. You see them on their way to work, school, or shopping. In contrast, bicyclists in the United States are mainly young people who bike for exercise or sport on the weekends.

Why do only a few Americans use the bike as a useful, non-polluting mode of transportation? It may be because we have a much lower density of people in the United States. Our cities and workplaces are usually far from our suburban homes, and so we have to travel longer distances to get to our destinations. In the United States, few roads have bike paths, and many Americans consider it dangerous to bike alongside busy traffic.

Our transportation modes might change if there were as many bike paths and sidewalks in the United States as there are in European countries. Bikers today have a hard time sharing the lanes with fast cars on the road, just as people who try to walk do. In such a car-oriented culture as ours, many Americans will continue to drive until we change our streets to accommodate walkers and bikers.

How Our Car Culture Began

One out of every two Americans has a car. Cars are so relatively plentiful that one in three cars in the world is owned by an American. Some of us have two or three cars parked in our garages.

How did we become such a colony of cars?

According to the 1996 documentary film *Taken for a Ride*, produced by Joe Klein and Martha Olson and shown on public television stations, when the automobile was still relatively in its infant stages in the 1920's, automaker General Motors bought many of the streetcars that were in operation. In 1922, only one American in ten owned an automobile. Nearly everyone else used the electric streetcars in urban areas, as they lived within walking distance of the streetcar line.

While Henry Ford was churning out over a million cars a day and making the car affordable to the middle class, the federal government gave huge subsidies to make roads and state highways.

Taken for a Ride reports that General Motors' president Alfred Sloan saw that if he eliminated the train market in the United States, he would create a new market for cars. Between 1936-1950, Sloan bought 100 electric streetcars in 45 cities and made the cities buy GM manufactured buses, thinking Americans would tire of the slow buses and feel the need to buy a car.

GM was successful despite the anti-trust and monopoly lawsuits brought against it. In 1949, GM and its partners were convicted of criminal conspiracy in the United States district court of Chicago and fined $5,000, but the fine failed to stop the company. The rest is history. The American driving culture was born.

The American housing industry, delayed by the Depression in the 1930's, began to build around the car after World War II. Realtors and land developers promoted and built suburbs far beyond city limits with only roads for individual transport and no mass transit links. Thus, many of our neighborhoods today are without access to services unless we have a car.

Traffic, Signs and Parking

When we talk about heavy traffic, it sounds like English as a foreign language with the slang the newscaster uses. Traffic jams are called *gridlock, stop-and-go* and *bumper-to-bumper traffic*. A *bottleneck* is when two roads merge and cause traffic congestion.

Traffic lights, arrows and signs point in different directions and seem to contradict themselves at intersections. Sometimes, you have to guess which sign to follow or else you can decide to go in the direction of the car in front of you.

On American highways, a series of signs for the same destination can make you dizzy. If you are going to the city of Great Neck, for instance, the sign reads, "Great Neck 5 miles," then, "Great Neck 4 miles," and signs continue to appear until the final, "Great Neck Exit." How many signs do we need for Great Neck?

Parking lots have spaces reserved for the handicapped, just as buses and trolleys have seating in the front. You'll be fined almost four hundred dollars if you park in the blue handicapped spot. Many seniors get a handicapped permit because they can't walk very far and need to park in the closest spots next to the store.

Since the handicapped permit gives access to the top parking spots, members of the family may use this permit also even though they are not handicapped in any way. This is why you may see very-able bodied teenagers pull up and park in a handicapped spot. While grandmother or mother might have a physical problem, they certainly don't. The police do not check who uses the permit but only look to see if the blue and white sign is clearly visible from the outside of the car.

Public Transportation

Why is the American public transportation system one of the worst in the industrialized world?

Seventy five percent of Americans drive alone to their jobs, while only 4.7 percent use public transportation and 0.4 percent bike to work. We have a crisis in intercity travel and mass transit in the United States.

Americans who live in the suburbs, according to studies, will use mass transit only when and if it is a real alternative to cars, such as trains and buses linking airports, schools, and a thorough network of public transportation.

What are the alternatives to driving in the United States?

It looks pretty grim.

How many cities even have a choice? Compared to Europe and Japan, we hardly have any trains yet alone high-speed trains. There is Amtrak, the only passenger train that offers interstate travel. Created in 1971, it is extremely expensive and serves only certain areas of the United States. Trains are practically invisible in this country, because they are mostly used for carrying freight. Trains carry 40% of the total freight, while the rest of the freight is still carried over land by heavy trucks. These trucks, competing with traffic on our highways, damage our roads and bridges. That has made us appear like the Romans; we build roads and bridges, dig them up and constantly repair them. The automakers have won the favor of the federal government, which gives massive subsidies to highways but very little funding to maintain trains or subsidize mass transit.

Only a handful of American cities have major subway

systems: New York City, San Francisco, Boston, Philadelphia, Washington D.C., Chicago, and a few other cities. Most of the cities in the Midwest, the South, and the West have no subways at all.

Buses in most of the country are incredibly slow and mainly serve the downtown areas of cities. Because of the limited areas served, buses have become the main transport of the poor and the elderly. Greyhound, the bus line that goes to other states, serves more areas and meets the need for cheap transportation. Students and immigrants are frequent Greyhound travelers, but many of its bus stations are in parts of inner cities that some people consider dangerous.

Many American cities are building light rail systems, but they are expensive to build and operate at slow speeds. They are also unable to move a lot of people in the short period of time that is needed for today's labor force.

Cities in other countries are at the forefront of alternatives to the car. In Tokyo, fast trains transport millions of people efficiently. In Brazil, the city of Curitiba has a unique bus system. Buses run on dedicated streets and provide low-cost service. In Basel, Switzerland, the city is heavily dependent on a tram system, and parts of the town are car-free. The Netherlands leads the world in the number of bicycle paths. And of course, the Italian cities of Rome, Florence, and Milan are walking cities because cars are banned in the downtown areas and the streets are completely filled with pedestrians.

Laws forcing drivers to leave their cars home by closing the centers of congested cities, or making drivers pay if they enter the downtown area, exist in various cities already. For example, London and Hong Kong are cities where drivers have to pay to enter the city.

Until Americans either build mass transit infrastructures to link people across the small towns and suburbs of the United States or force us to leave our cars at home, we will continue to be married to our cars.

The Buzz on Beauty

Hot Spots for Cosmetic Surgery

Bangkok, Thailand – Bangkok Preecha Aesthetic Institute.

Seoul, Korea – The Apkujong section of Seoul is well-known for its reasonable rates and high quality surgeons, also known as the "Plastic Surgery Street."

Brazil – Brazil has 3,200 plastic surgeons, second only to the United States with 6,100.

What Westerners Want
slimmer bodies
wrinkle-free skin
fuller breasts

What Asians Want
wider eyes
longer noses
slimmer cheeks

The Most Beautiful Women

The countries that have won the most Miss Universe and Miss World Titles combined: Venezuela (9 times), India (7 times), Sweden, (6 times).

Job Interviews in Korea and Japan

In Korea, because the job market is so competitive, there is a growing trend of recent graduates having cosmetic surgery to look better and therefore, have a competitive edge in their job interviews. In Japan, this happens too. It is called recruit *seikei*.

Chapter 13:

Beauty Marks

Have your ever seen what you think is a beautiful woman walking in front of you, she turns around, and surprise! She's sixty years old with wrinkles on her face! There are sixty-year-olds walking around in twenty-year old bodies. You shouldn't assume that when people age in the United States they will turn ugly or fat and stay at home. Many seniors keep in good shape and lead active lifestyles.

For older American women, we have the euphemism of "growing old gracefully." This is considered a compliment and means you can be both beautiful and old.

The actress Katherine Hepburn was a model of aging beauty. Cosmetic companies market expensive creams to women to postpone this natural aging process. These beauty companies are now marketing to men for the first time. Beauty products geared to men were not needed in the past since there has always been a double standard about attractiveness as men and women age. Men have been valued both young and wrinkled but women have had to look young for the rest of their lives. How people view the aging process is a reflection of the values in a culture.

Who sets the beauty standards in the United States? Movie and television actresses, singers, Miss America winners and fashion models are *the beautiful people* in this culture. They are the role models that women seek to copy for their hairstyles, body structure and fashion.

Our beautiful people reveal the secret physical features Americans value. Look at the dolls sold in the United States. Barbie dolls, which came out in 1957, are still the most common dolls you see in children's bedrooms. Barbie was the first doll that wasn't an imitation of a baby. A doll that was a young woman who had big breasts and a boyfriend named Ken was revolutionary at the time.

Mirror, mirror on the wall, who is beautiful in the eyes of all? No one. There is no uniform standard of beauty in the United States, but the big-breasted blonde with fair skin and blue eyes remains a beauty ideal for many white women. Although there is pressure to conform to this mainstream concept of beauty, Asians, Hispanics and African Americans have their own ideals of beauty within their own communities.

For the Barbie doll wannabes, you have to be thin, and when you're thin, you usually don't have a big chest. You see women searching to be Barbies today in the lingerie section of department stores. Flat-chested, they scout for a padded bra or the push up Wonder Bras. If they have enough money, they are somewhere in a cosmetic surgeon's office undergoing surgery for silicone implants.

A sizeable number of American women wish to be blonde because they think men find blondes more attractive and sexier than brunettes. Where does this idea that blonde is better come from? Joanna Pitman in her book *On Blondes*, traces the origin of blonde hair as a symbol of beauty to the Greeks. She writes that the concept is more than two thousand years old and began with the Greek goddess of love, Aphrodite, who was blonde. During the Renaissance, the word "fair" became synonymous with beautiful in the English language.

Today, we export the myth that American women have blonde hair and blue eyes. Why are we so fixated on blonde hair? We are a youth-oriented culture and many people associate blonde hair with youth. Many babies are born with blonde hair but gradually their turns darker as they grow older. Over time, adults began to associate blonde hair with youth and fertility and it grew into an aesthetic and cultural preference.

When foreigners visit the United States, many are surprised to see the many hair colors American women really have.

Only 7 percent of American women colored their hair in 1950, and they did it mainly to cover up the gray with their natural color. Today, it is estimated that around 50% of American women color their hair. Coloring your hair for fashion's sake is popular with young, middle-aged, and older women today. Women no longer have to feel that the hair color must match their natural hair color as much as possible to disguise the fact that they are coloring it. Now American men are joining the ranks and coloring their hair in growing numbers.

Very few blondes in the United States are naturally blonde. Only one in every twenty blonde American adults in the United States is genuinely blonde while the others bleach their hair. The hair coloring industry makes a fortune off American women who want to be blonde because our culture gives a certain status to blondes.

Madonna is a natural brunette but attributes part of her success to turning blonde. For her *True Blue* album in 1986, she appeared on the cover for the first time as a bleached-blonde. More than 20 million copies sold worldwide compared to her as a brunette on previous albums that sold only 5 million copies. Madonna

Good-Looking American Men

American women generally like beefy men and the stakes are high. Since 1990, steroids have been banned in the United States yet an estimated one million Americans, most of them men, use steroids to build muscle mass. No longer limited to athletes and body-builders, many American men lift weights in a gym to get that muscular look.

immediately recognized the commercial value of blonde hair and it became part of her star image. "Being blonde is definitely a different state of mind," Madonna told *Rolling Stone* magazine. "I can't really put my finger on it, but the artifice of being blonde has some incredible sort of sexual connotation."

Women from other countries are not immune to wanting to be blonde. They watch blonde stars on *Sex in the City* and *Friends*, read *Cosmopolitan* and *Glamour* and aspire to the Western standard of beauty. No matter how naturally black their hair is in Japan, thousands of young women use peroxide there to become blonde. Some do it out of rebellion; others do it because they want to look more Western. In Brazil as well, many women turn blonde despite the fact that very few Brazilians are naturally blonde.

African American women judge a woman's beauty by her hair. As the major consumers of hair products in the United States, black women style their hair creatively into braids, twists and locks. They use flatirons, hot combs, curling irons, and rollers, and an assortment of gels. The fashion model Naomi Campbell and film actress Halle Berry have been beauty ideals for many African American women. Studies also have shown that African American women have a healthier attitude toward their bodies than white women, as they have a very low incidence of bulimia and anorexia.

Hispanic women usually think they are more beautiful wearing makeup. They are heavy users of lipstick, foundation, powder and eyeliner. Jennifer Lopez has been a role model for many Hispanic women. She has started her own line of perfume. The Hispanic beauty ideal is also curvier than the white woman's image. The Hispanic film, *Real Woman Have Curves*, is about this acceptance of a fuller body.

Asian Americans value skin that is the color of milk. They buy whitening creams in search of ivory skin in a jar.

They slather on the sunscreen, wear visors, and carry umbrellas for royal protection from the sun. They also value being thin, which is skinnier than most other Americans aspire to; the skinnier, the better.

Unlike the pale skin ideal of the past, white women in the United States today want a sun-kissed face in the United States. The trend is catching on in Asian countries, too. Many women think having a tan makes them look healthy and rich, like Hollywood stars. Drugstores sell bronzed skin in a bottle, and both men and women flock to tanning salons to lie under a lamp or get sprayed with a chemical. Tanned skin has become a status symbol. It is associated with leisure time outdoors today, unlike in the past when it was associated with the lower class working in the fields. If you have time to play sports or lay out on the beach in this business world, you must have money to maintain your year-round tan.

What is rare in the culture often becomes the gold standard for beauty. In Brazil, women want bigger chests, in Japan and Korea, double eyelids and a narrow nose. In the United States, American women want to be thin and young forever, and the most common cosmetic surgeries are liposuction and Botox.

Being thin is a status symbol and is associated with economic success in many countries. In the United States, there is a saying, "You can never be too thin or too rich."

Beauty contests also set unrealistic beauty standards for most women. The average American woman is 5 feet and 4 inches tall (1.64 meters) and weighs 140 lbs. (63.5 kilos). The average Miss America contestant is 5 feet and 8 inches tall (1.73 meters) and weighs 120 lbs. (54 kilos). Only 10% of American women fit the height and weight profile of a professional model. Seven million young women suffer from eating disorders in the United States, and the number is increasing, according to the National Association of Anorexia Nervosa and Associated Eating Disorders (ANAD).

Our eating and exercise habits have not kept pace with the beauty standards in our heads. Most women read fashion magazines or watch the Miss America pageant and feel bad about themselves. We can't compare to the air-brushed or televised models. Through camera and makeup tricks, pounds have melted off the model, makeup has erased her lines on her forehead, and for that matter, any freckles and pimples too.

Just when we become dissatisfied with ourselves, women's magazines advertise "self-esteem." You mean we can look like our models and movie stars displayed on their covers? How do we manage this? Buy these cosmetics, go on this diet, take this vitamin, and we will make ourselves over like Cinderella going to the ball.

Too many bad hair days? A first-rate haircut at this expensive salon, or a $20-dollar gel will make us look like Jennifer Aniston. The cosmetic and hair-care industry convinces American women to constantly change their appearance by spending more money to be beautiful.

Some American women wear quite a bit of makeup, especially eye-shadows, compared to other countries. We put unnatural blues, glittery pinks and other colors on our eyelids that many women from other countries find strange. American women also wear bright red, purple and even glitter nail polish. False fingernails or acrylics are quite common among women. Others paint their nails one color and then put tattoos or designs on top of the nail polish.

A few American magazines have broken with the traditional view of beauty. Instead of putting only thin women on their covers they have included overweight models. Clothing lines for plus-size women are growing in the fashion industry. As sixty percent of Americans are overweight, magazines featuring full-figure models more accurately portray American women today.

Most American women consider men such as Tom Cruise and Denzel Washington classically handsome. Both actors have highly defined jaws and with no beard or mustache. They look like the eternal college student, or what Americans call clean-cut or preppy.

The average American male is 5' 10" inches (1.78 meters) tall and weighs 180 lbs. (82 kilos). Many American women like tall and muscular men. Men sweat in gyms so that their biceps pop out like two tennis balls. They believe the meatier they are, the more handsome they will be.

Fashion

Fashion in the United States is often a matter of wearing jeans, a T-shirt and tennis shoes 90% of the time. Sweat suits made for jogging are now worn to shopping malls, school and just about everywhere except work.

We Americans compare ourselves to French culture all the time, yet the rest of the world knows us for our "low-brow" culture of costume jewelry and sports clothes. We wear white socks with our tennis shoes everywhere. In many European countries, white socks are strictly used for sports or in farming regions. You would be seen as on your way to the tennis court, for example, and not to the movies.

Michael Jordan and Madonna did more for the fashion industry in the United States than many of our fashion models put together. Jordan started the baggy pants craze in the 1980's when he wore his basketball uniform under his regular pants with a big belt and a fad was born.

Madonna changed fashion forever when she brought bras out of the underwear drawer and wore them publicly. Today, we have many shirts that are camisoles which in pre-Madonna days, would have been considered lingerie for the bedroom.

American casual clothes can shock you with the intensity and choice of colors. T-shirts, in particular, have developed into an art form in the United States. They come in bright orange, hot pink, and loud green. You can find them with bold stripes, advertising decals and political slogans. Messages are often offensive, or they are walking advertisements for a company in the form of brands and logos.

Business attire is more casual here than in Europe and Asia, but it varies with the region. On the East Coast, the suit coat and tie are still worn, and East Coast women wear more neutral colors. Black is seen in New York City more than other parts of the country. In the South, you see more floral designs, dresses and hats. In the West, business attire can be khakis and a polo shirt for men, and suits can be even worn with cowboy boots in the ranching states.

On the West Coast in particular, men in insurance and real estate often wear a nicely pressed shirt and wool pants, but they leave the tie home or the suit coat in the office when they go to lunch. If you look too fashionable in California, people think you look overdressed. Many employees love Fridays as it is often a "dress down" day. This is when you can even wear jeans to work.

Doggies, Kitties & Birdies

Chapter 14:

Pets as Partners

Sixty-two percent of American households own a pet, according to a 2001/2002 survey by the American Pet Products Manufacturers Association. We are truly a pet loving nation. Many Americans view pets as a member of the family, even as partners. More than half of American dog owners are more attached to their pets than to another human being, reports the American Pet Association in 2003. Most American dogs sleep in the bed with their owners and 67% of America's cats do. And some 39% of America's pet owners display their pet's picture in their home.

Americans love a variety of pets, but most of all, we love our dogs. We kiss dogs on the mouth, give them manicures and throw them birthday parties. We have doggie beaches and bakeries. We have plastic bags provided by beaches and parks to clean up dog waste.

American customs and attitudes toward their dogs and cats are based on our own personal needs. The explosion

Out of the Doghouse...

and into the Beauty Parlor...

Pet Signature Clothing – Dress your pet in style.

Pet Massages – To rejuvenate muscles and joints.

Pet Sitters – Drop off your pet at a daycare center or at a friend's house.

Pet Videos – When you are away at work, your pet no longer has to feel lonely.

Pet Beauty Line – *Fauna*, a Santa-Monica based company offers all-natural bath line for pets. Stamped with people tested, pet-approved.

Pet Health Insurance – To insure against the high cost of illness and accidents.

Pet Nail Polish – OPI, a leading nail polish brand for women, has now designed nail polish specifically for pets' nails. It is called Pet Pawlish. Now pet owners can give their pets a beautiful pet-i-cure.

of pets seems to show how lonely we are as a nation for companionship. Families are getting smaller and a growing number of singles, childless couples and older people look to a pet to keep them company.

Historically, the Christian religion has believed in the dominion of humans over animals. Today, however, animals have been raised a notch on the human scale as a growing number of Americans treat them as children. When we talk to them, we often say "Good boy!" and "Good girl!" instead of "Good dog! or "Good cat!"

Laws are being adapted to the changing ways of thinking about pets in the United States. Pet trusts are becoming popular in a growing number of states. Currently, nineteen of the fifty states allow pet owners to set up a trust fund for the care, feeding and medical treatment of their pets if the owners die.

Colorado, in particular, has been leading the way to change the status of pets as property and make them domestic companions. A law is being considered that would allow people in Colorado to sue veterinarians or animal abusers and seek damages of up to $100,000 for "loss of companionship." If this law passes, it would be the first companionship law in the United States.

With new pet-guardian legislation coming in the future, pet owners may seek damages against negligent veterinarians and, in turn, insurance rates for veterinarians will rise.

Americans spend $150 million a year on pet pain medicines alone and more and more pet owners are investing in pet health insurance. We are prolonging pet lifespans with medicines that have been traditionally reserved for humans. Pets in the United States get radiation therapy, hip replacements, organ transplants and high-tech diagnostic procedures such as magnetic resonance imaging. Specialized veterinary medicine is a booming industry.

There is even a new airline catering to pets,

Companion Air, which has recently begun operating in the United States. People can be seated with their pets in the plane's cabin, unlike other major airlines, which put large animals in the cargo hold.

Animal shelters have been set up in the United States for abused pets. You can call a government protection agency for pets. If a neighbor reports signs of pet abuse, the animal control agency will come and may take the pet away to an animal shelter to protect it.

Cats and dogs that seem to be without owners are seen less frequently in the United States than in other countries. If a stray dog or cat is seen roaming the street in the United States, someone in the neighborhood usually calls the local Animal Control agency and an official comes to fetch the animal and take it to an animal shelter too. Since there are too many dogs and pets in the United States, animal shelters are forced to kill hundreds of thousands of dogs and cats each year.

Disney animated movies help very little in controlling our impulse to buy a pet we might not be able to take care of. They show cute animals that talk and sing, which motivates some Americans to go out and buy a pet shown in the movie. Clown fish sold briskly in pet stores when the movie *Finding Nemo* was released.

When the movie *101 Dalmatians* came out some years ago, it caused people to run to the pet store and scoop up a frisky Dalmatian dog. Many of these impulsive owners eventually gave these animals to the animal shelters, as they realized, over time, that they couldn't take care of them.

Becoming a vegetarian is the ultimate statement in favor of animals for some people. Many vegetarians in the United States eat no meat, not for health reasons but for the love of animals.

Animal rights activists in the United States have been very influential in elevating pets to near human status. These groups target different animals to be saved, organize campaigns and are highly visible as they get out on the streets and protest. They first started out opposing animals being used for fur by throwing paint and blood on the fur coats of fashionable ladies coming out of department stores. Now, very few Americans wear real fur. Another issue was dolphins being trapped in tuna fishermen's nets.

Animal rights groups won that battle too. Now tuna cans sold in the United States are labeled *"dolphin-safe."* Animal testing for cosmetics has greatly decreased and now many of our shampoo bottles and cosmetic packages print *"no animal testing."*

The activities of the animal rights groups, however, are turning more violent. The Animal Liberation Front, or the ALF, is now on the FBI's list of domestic terrorist groups. Ecological groups and animal-rights extremists have been responsible for an estimated 1,100 violent acts since 1976, the FBI reported in a hearing before Congress. The violent tactics of the animal extremists focus their attacks on medical and research labs at universities.

Attitudes toward dogs vary according to culture. In Muslim countries, they are largely seen as unclean and a source of spreading diseases. In Singapore, Hong Kong and South Korea, dog soup is considered a hearty soup. In Latin America, they are not treated the same as in the United States. You see many stray dogs that people kick out of their way walking down the street. Stray dogs roaming in the street are seen as dangerous and aggressive.

You hear stories of children being bitten by these stray dogs and so many people are afraid of dogs. In Asian countries, space largely dictates the kind of pet you can have. Fish and birds are more common than dogs and cats, as they take up less space. Pets any bigger than hamsters are forbidden in most Japanese apartments. Also, Japan is very hygiene conscious, and if the Japanese have a dog, they usually don't sleep with their owners.

However, the trend of owning a pet is a growing phenomenon in other countries too. Traditionally, dogs and cats have been fed the leftovers or food scraps off the dinner table, without buying commercial pet food in the stores. But now, pet food sales are exploding, reports the Pet Food Institute. The Korean market for pet food alone has increased 600 percent over the past 10 years. Latin America is buying more pet food too, as pet ownership is becoming more popular, and feeding pets commercially prepared food is on the rise.

Notes

"Acquiring a dog may be the only time a person gets to choose a relative."

– Unknown

Got Checks?

To Pay Bills
Most Americans write personal checks at home and send the checks by mail.

7-Eleven Convenience Stores
While 7-Elevens are known in the U.S. for its huge soft-drinks like Big Gulps and Slurpees, in Thailand and Japan, people pay electric and telephone bills there.

Post Offices
In many European and Asian countries, you can do banking at the post office or in some cases, even pay bills there too.

Got Cash?

ATMs in cash-oriented countries can give out more cash to their bank customers than in the U.S.

In Latin American countries, credit cards are usually limited to high-income individuals because interest rates are quite high.

Chapter 15:

Dreaming of Dollars

W hy is it that millions of dollars can be transmitted instantly across the globe by satellite, yet within the United States interstate banking barely exists? A California bank can't transfer money to a Michigan bank without a time-consuming and costly application process to open a new account in that state.

Another paradox is that we often have a credit card limit of thousands of U.S. dollars but banks' automated teller machines usually allow a maximum of $300 cash a day to be withdrawn. Many Americans do not even apply for such a high credit card limit. Usually, a letter comes in the mail that informs us our credit card line has been increased. In other words, we now have the chance to get ourselves into more debt.

Americans are noted for being spenders, not savers. Why should we put savings in the bank? The average interest on a savings account in American banks ranges from only 1 to 2%, while inflation is running an average of 4-6%.

Special Treatment and Tipping

In a society where everyone is supposed to be treated equally, Americans secretly want to be treated special, like a king or queen. Ask us about our vacations, and instead of describing the places and people, we'll begin to tell you about all the luxuries of the beautiful hotel with a swimming pool, and the way people treated us like royalty.

We are the biggest tippers in the world because we tip to show how well servers treated us more than how fast they served us. While most countries have a service charge included in the restaurant bill or a much smaller tip such as 10%, we have a 15-20% "voluntary donation." Many international visitors reluctantly tip if the service is good but what happens if the service is bad? A tip of 10% or less usually makes a statement that the service was poor.

The word *tips* is said to have originated from an acronym, "to insure prompt service," dating back to sixteenth-century England. Customers would give the waiter money *before* they were served, and the tip amount would determine how well they were treated.

The quality of the service in restaurants in the United States greatly depends on the individual server who waits on you. You might get servers who take a long time to bring your meal and look overworked. Then there are the overenthusiastic servers whose presentation of the daily specials resembles performance art. They eagerly give us so many options that we cannot remember any particular dish.

Americans usually tip whether or not the service was poor or even when there were too many interruptions by an overeager waiter. We generally feel sorry for the low wages that waiters earn, which is usually close to minimum wage plus tips. Tips have spread to fast-food eateries and self-service cafes. Today, you may see a giant jar for tips next to the cash register, even though no one has given you personal table service.

Money Habits

Americans talk about money freely when it relates to the state of the economy or how much things cost in general. Yet our own money is considered nobody's business, and subject of personal finances is considered a taboo topic.

In many families, only the mother and father discuss money and manage the household finances. They don't inform the children. Young people get their first job as teenagers and begin to manage their money with little guidance. We have learned to spend through an allowance, but we have not been taught to save. The majority of Americans households, 74%, are in debt, and are paying on mortgages, car loans or credit cards. In addition, Americans owe an average of $2,000 on their credit cards, according to the Statistical Abstract of the U.S. 2001.

Many Americans try to become rich and famous as quickly as possible. We play the lottery or gamble in casinos, not only in Las Vegas but also on Indian reservations or off-shore ships. On TV, *Joe Millionaire* was a popular show among young people. Women wanted to date this American bachelor who was supposed to be a millionaire. When the women in the contest found out that the bachelor wasn't a millionaire after all, most of them were disillusioned and lost interest in him.

Learning Annex, a school for working adults, offers classes such as, "Smart Couples Finish Rich," "How to Think Like the Rich," "Make $$$ as a Researcher," "Earn a $1,000 a day as a Personal Coach," and "How to Hide Your Assets and Disappear."

Americans love to hear stories of people from humble beginnings who become rich from their hard work and personal initiative. In school, we learn about Abraham Lincoln and other heroes who went from rags to riches. Parents ask children what they want to be when they are growing up. A doctor? A lawyer? They tell their children that they can be anything they want regardless of talent or economic limitations.

Then when young people graduate from high school and take their first full-time job, they become disillusioned. Many earn minimum wage. Weren't they going to be rich and famous just like their parents and schools told them?

When foreigners see an American writing a check for less than $10 in the supermarket, they are amazed. Why are Americans so attached to checks? We still use checks when other countries use cash, pay online, or by credit card. In fact, the United States was the only country that saw growth in check use in today's world of electronic banking.

The average American writes 15 checks a month, according to a recent Federal Reserve report. Sixty percent of our non-cash transactions are with a check. We pay most of our bills with a check and send it through the mail. In many countries in Latin America, the people go in person to the post offices or utility companies to pay their bills.

In Europe, debit and credit cards are more widely used than here. In some Western European countries, people must pay a small fee to write a check. This charge discourages people from writing checks. Americans like the fact that there is a time lapse of about a day before the check is cashed.

Even American retailers like checks, now that they have a little machine to verify that the funds to cover the check are in the customer's bank account. With this machine, the cost of processing a check is cheaper than processing a credit card.

The American dollar is also called a "buck." This nickname for the dollar can be traced to our colonial days, when we used buckskins, or the hides of a male deer, as a money substitute. Compared to the colorful paper money of other countries, our dollar bills are not exactly exciting. The Eurobills, for example, display colorful architecture of member countries.

We have dead presidents and major political figures on one side of the bills and political buildings on the other.

Only once did a woman appear on a U.S. bill. Martha Washington, the wife of our founding president, appeared on $1 silver certificate in the late 1880's. We have failed to represent important women in our history on our bills, while countries such as Germany, Denmark, and Sweden have had many outstanding women depicted on their bills.

While most of our American bills are still monochrome green, this is changing. Our new $20 note features background colors of green, peach and blue on both sides. New colorful designs for the $50, $10, and $5 bills are to be issued in the future.

For coins, the United States once minted a silver dollar with a woman on it. Susan B. Anthony, a leader in the 19th century women's rights movement, was the first woman to appear on a coin. Many Americans didn't like or use the silver coin because they confused it with the quarter, and so it has largely gone out of circulation. You can, however, still get Susan Anthony dollars as change from the stamp vending machines at U.S. post offices.

Recently, the United States issued a second coin with a woman on it. This time it was a gold coin and bigger than the quarter. Sacagawea, an Indian woman with her child strapped to her back, appears on the gold dollar coin. She was instrumental to the success of the Lewis and Clark expedition and the exploration of the Missouri River. This coin can be requested at local banks, and is also available at post offices whose stamp vending machines give change in coins.

Status or Pay?

There is a major difference between the social status of a job and what it pays in the U.S. as shown below in the two tables.

The Most Prestigious Jobs	*The Best Paid Jobs*
1. Scientist	1. Doctor
2. Doctor	2. Lawyer
3. Military Officer	3. Airplane Pilot
4. Teacher	4. Aerospace Engineer
5. Police Officer	5. Pharmacist
6. Priest/Minister/Clergy	6. Chemical Engineer
7. Engineer	7. Electronic Engineer
8. Architect	8. Mechanical Engineer
9. Congressman	9. Marketing & PR
10. Athlete	10. Architect

Source: U.S. Bureau of Labor Statistics and Harris Poll 2002

Chapter 16:

Work: 24/7

Why do Americans work so hard? Many people think the Protestant work ethic drives Americans to work long hours. This may have been the case in the past, but not anymore. Companies have been downsizing, and threat of getting laid off is very real today. Americans now work longer hours, and often do the work of two or three people because they are afraid of losing their jobs. They work hard to become valuable to the company so that if and when the company lays off employees, the boss will keep them on staff.

How obsessed are Americans with work? This can be measured if you take a day off. If you happen to run into someone on the street while doing errands, they will ask you, "You mean you're not working today?" That may lead to, "Are you still working at the same place?" to confirm you are not laid off.

Your job identifies you more than anything else in the United States, except for race or ethnicity. Americans question each other, and the questions usually follow a certain order, such as, "What's your name?" Then if you look physically different or have a foreign-sounding name, it will be followed by, "Where are you from?" We continue with our identification process until we get to, "What do you do?"

The most powerful excuse you can give someone when they invite you somewhere and you would rather not go is, "I have to work." No more questions will be asked. The other person will understand and think work always comes before a social engagement. Compare this to, "I'm busy." You might get more questions as to when your appointment is and insistence that you come after your social commitment.

In the United States, you can be hired relatively easily, compared to other countries. Many people do not have employment contracts in the United States. When workers are hired for a job, their salary, working hours and benefits are often discussed in the hiring interview. At the end of this interview, the employer and the new employee trust each other with a simple verbal agreement called a "gentlemen's agreement" when it is followed by a handshake. Some employers, however, require you to have a medical exam, a background check, or a second interview before they will actually hire you.

Getting fired or dismissed is fairly easy too. Usually, an employee is given two chances to make major mistakes, through a verbal and a written warning. If the work performance hasn't changed by the third time, an employer can fire them. Policies toward work performance and behavior vary widely, but many workplaces have a "zero tolerance" policy for alcohol and drug use. If employers catch an employee working either while drinking or high on drugs, it is possible that the employee could be fired immediately.

If you are unemployed in the United States, you usually use up your savings, if you have any. You can file for unemployment, but the federal government gives you money for just six months. A check for unemployment is usually less than half of the salary you earned, so it is an impossible amount to survive on.

Many Americans do not have a family network to help them in times of job loss and so we work doubly hard. We tend not to have much savings either, and so we commonly say, "We don't have anything to fall back on."

We work an average of 40 hours a week, census data shows, but this doesn't reflect the reality of work today. With the Internet and cell phone an integral part of the work day, we now have the tools to take our job home. We also bring our laptops to work on the plane, on the beach, in bed, and even on vacation. We have "working lunches," "working dinners," and "working vacations." Our work day has stretched into many unofficial hours, averaging another 10-20 hours a week with our electronic cords.

You often hear that time is money in the United States. Even though you hear Americans complain about never having enough time, money is actually more important than time to us, according to a recent Roper survey. When the survey gave a choice between more money or more time, 56% of Americans chose money, while only 35% wanted more time.

The computer has been quickly replacing jobs in the United States, as it is in other countries. However, in the United States, the manufacturing sector has been moving abroad at a rapid pace to reduce labor costs. American corporations have been able to lay off workers with relative ease without paying employees severance pay or medical insurance.

This differs from other countries where labor laws or government controls are stronger. Labor unions have been decreasing steadily since the 1940's. Only 13% of the American workplace is unionized, mainly in the auto, construction, and mining industries. When we know that a computer can replace us at any time, we are demoralized and our loyalty to a company is affected. We are apt to change jobs more frequently as we see our jobs as disposable.

Entire occupations have been lost to the electronic scanner alone. Price clerks and grocery clerks are being replaced with the customers scanning the store items themselves. Self-serve restaurants have replaced waitresses.

Gas station and parking attendants have virtually disappeared. Software programs are taking the job of purchasing agents as a program signals to the supplier when the store needs new orders. Automated teller machines, or ATMs, have taken away bank teller jobs.

The camera is another example of a technology that has taken away many security guards' and police officers' jobs. The police no longer have to wait by a traffic light because a camera can do all the work. In an effort to make police work safer and more cost-effective, the Chicago police have started to use video cameras that are mounted on lampposts in neighborhoods with gangs. A police officer parks his car in another location and watches the monitors.

Full-time jobs are disappearing in the United States as part-time and temporary workers are skyrocketing. Firms cut labor costs and increase flexibility by hiring these kinds of workers, who typically receive no benefits. Part-time workers make up 18% percent of our work force and are increasing. The Bureau of Labor Statistics reports 35 million temporary workers, or nearly one third of our labor force, is made up of temporary workers.

Balancing Work and Family

Sixty percent of American women work, reports the Bureau of Labor Statistics 2002. Many of these women are also mothers. The American workplace, however, has still a long way to go in order to meet the needs of working mothers. It has only been since 1993 that a woman could take three months off for unpaid maternity leave and be guaranteed her job back when she returned.

A federal law called the Family and Medical Leave Act now gives American workers up to 12 weeks a year of unpaid leave to take care of a family member. This policy allows American employees time to have a baby or take care of an elderly parent. The employer, by law, must reserve their positions and seniority in the company until the employees return. This law, however, only applies to companies with 50 or more employees. Since most companies in the United States have fewer than 50 employees, they are not legally obligated to offer this benefit to their workers.

Even when companies offer this benefit, few Americans take advantage of it. There is still the stigma attached to taking personal time off from your job that prevents workers from using this job benefit.

Child care for working parents is also scarce in the United States. There are not many daycare centers or preschools for working parents who have no family members living close by. There are even fewer daycare centers for children under two years old. The cost of insurance is so high for this age group that most daycare/preschools do not accept very young children. Therefore, many children under two years old are watched by home-based daycare workers. These daycares vary in quality and are often criticized for accepting too many children into one home. You only need minimum training to qualify as a daycare provider before you can set up your home for a babysitting operation. Many housewives earn a good living taking care of infants. The other alternative is for mothers to stay home these first two years. This, however, is not an option for many working families.

Time

Though time may not be as important as earning cash

Personal vs. Professional Life

Americans divide their lives into personal and professional. After working eight or more hours at the job or so-called "professional life," we usually go home to the "personal life" or family.

We usually do not wine or dine with colleagues after work. Bosses usually do not call employees at home unless it's an urgent matter.

I Quit!

Looking for another job is fairly common in the United States. Many Americans plan to change jobs every year, and most of us will have several employers in our lifetime. Americans stay on their jobs for an average of four years, according to the Bureau of Labor Statistics 2002.

Time or Money?

to an American, it is still considered extremely valuable. Future time is valued the most and what happened in the past is valued the least. You can see how the past is often dismissed. "That's history," you hear Americans say, "forget it. Today is different." Future time is valued because we think we can control it. Americans get irritated waiting in grocery lines and when they get caught in traffic because the waiting time is unpredictable and therefore, outside of our control.

When an unexpected tragedy occurs, whether it be wildfires or plane crashes, what is the official American response that you see published in the newspapers? It is not an emotional reaction but a measured one, "We are determining the cause of the accident. An investigation as to the cause has been ordered." We think we can still do something even when there is nothing to do.

The notion of a country living on future time is evident in the buying of insurance. We must buy car insurance by law, "in case we have an accident." Buying insurance of any sort calms us down and erases the worries of future accidents.

We have mortgage insurance "in case we lose our jobs." We have health insurance, "in case we get sick." We have life insurance, "in case we die and no one has money to hold a funeral and bury us properly." Some people even buy flight insurance "in case the plane goes down."

We have fire drills in schools and workplaces, "in case of a fire," and, in some parts of the country, "in case of an earthquake." This "in case of an accident" mentality is shortened in our minds and we often simply say, "just in case." The bad thing that could possibly happen is implied.

We sometimes justify buying many items in the supermarket or stores, stocking up, "just in case." The fear is that the store will stop carrying the item and you will return and be left without a choice.

Some Americans plan their vacations a year in advance and may buy airline tickets up to a month in advance.

International visitors and students are bothered when they want to make plans for a weekend in Las Vegas or San Francisco. After making some phone calls, they realize that the cheapest tickets must be purchased 14 days in advance. Two weeks? They want to go in two days. In some countries, the best rates can be had with one-week notice, and in other countries there is no discount for advance reservations, so planning in advance is not rewarded.

Wasting time is highly subjective. If you take a vacation and it's not heavily programmed into a schedule of activities, or you are not going out of town, Americans might consider it a waste of time.

Americans have agendas in their hands and calendars on their minds. Time is a product to the American psyche. We buy and spend it, borrow and lend it. There is a good time and a bad time to do something. "One thing at a time," we say when we want to slow things down. We find and lose time, set or schedule time. Something takes up time, and we make up time. We are behind or ahead of time according to the hands of a clock. We reward people for being on time. Most movie theaters and restaurants seat you on a first come, first served basis. Though many Americans tend to be punctual for work, we are much less so for personal engagements. Again, we want to control our time and choose our time of arrival over someone else's. For a social occasion, Americans will usually tolerate latecomers for a ten to fifteen-minute grace period before they leave, make new plans, or cancel reservations.

Measuring on an American Ruler

You walk into a McDonald's in France and there is no such thing as a "Quarter Pounder with Cheese." Instead, they offer a "Hamburger Royale with Cheese." The measurement of a quarter of a pound is not understood by most of the world, and it is like speaking a foreign tongue.

The United States is one of the few countries that

clings to the English Imperial system. Why doesn't the United States have the metric system when the rest of world does?

That is a question we have been trying to answer since we started to convert to the metric system in 1975, without much success. We first tried to convert the road signs to have both English miles and metric kilometers. What happened? We went back to the miles again. We never really changed. We just experimented with converting to the metric system.

It has been a constant battle, as our system is so tied to the beginning of our country. American colonists adopted the English or Imperial system of inches, pounds, and miles when our country first developed. The British system dates back to the reign of King Henry I (1100-1135) when the royal government made the 12-inch foot official.

The metric system, on the other hand, is much younger. It dates back only to the French Revolution of 1789. Great Britain, at that time was very anti-French and didn't want anything to do with French changes, and so the Imperial system continued in England and the United States, while the rest of the world adopted the much easier French measurement system where things can be divided by ten.

The U.S. federal government has been trying to lead the public by labeling food products with both the metric and the English system. The U.S. military has basically changed to the metric system too.

In the global economy, many Americans cannot measure properly today because they are taught two systems of measurement in our schools. Our system is much harder to learn. With three feet to a yard and 12 inches to a foot, the base number of 10 in the metric system is easier. We are taught metric too, but very briefly, and the end result of this two-tracked system is that many students can't measure accurately in either system.

Some scholars believe that our clinging to the English

measurement system has hurt American students when they compete against international students in math and science tests. On the Third International Math and Science Test, American students had to do all the math work in metric. This worked to their disadvantage, as many are not proficient in that measurement system. If they had grown up with the metric system, they might have done better on the math portion and would have been more competitive with their international counterparts.

If the United States goes metric, it will shake up not only the educational system, but will also radically change the way we do many things here. It's in our English vocabulary. In traffic, "We haven't moved an inch." (At all.) In complaining, "If you give an inch, they take a mile." (If you give a little to someone, they will take a lot.)

All our football fields would have to be lengthened in our stadiums, going to 100 meters instead of 100 yards. Even when the National Football League started a European League, the fields were measured in yards.

Though the sport of track has already changed to metric, people still refer to the 880 or the 220, which are English units, not metric. Although the races are in metric distances, the field events, such as the high jump, long jump, and pole vault, still use the English system.

Construction contractors would have to change the way they measure to build houses and commercial buildings. It would require every tool and piece of equipment made in the United States to be torn apart and refigured in metric parts.

Going metric would take a huge investment of money in the short term, but in the long term it would save Americans money. It would eliminate the costly two-system approach and help us master one measurement system rather than being mediocre in both. As far as competing in a global economy, it would make trade easier with our international counterparts and deepen our understanding of our global partners.

Notes

*"The best way to appreciate your job is
to imagine yourself without one."*

– Oscar Wilde, humorist (1856-1900)

I Pledge Allegiance

I pledge allegiance
To the flag
Of the United States of America,
And to the Republic
For which it stands,
One nation,
Under God,
Indivisible,
With liberty and justice for all.

Chapter 17:

Flag Fever

W hy are Americans so patriotic? The American flag waves to us from front porches, car antennas, and hotel rooftops. We wear flag pins on our coats and t-shirts. Signs in people's windows read, "Proud to be an American."

Most Americans do love their country and are proud of it, polls report.

Although Americans take pride in their individuality, when we show our patriotism, we act with a group mentality like never before. Many people display the U.S. flag outside their homes for patriotic holidays.

Our patriotism is often judged by flying or swearing to our flag. We stand up and sing the national anthem before sporting events. Students must face the flag and swear to be loyal to their country from elementary through high school with the Pledge of Allegiance. Immigrants who become naturalized citizens swear to be loyal to the United States and give up all their loyalty to their country of origin.

The American Soldier

The Privileged   Status of a Soldier

- ○ Free room and board or tax-free housing
- ○ A monthly salary
- ○ Free medical and dental care
- ○ A military clothing allowance
- ○ Military shopping privileges
- ○ 30 days of paid vacation a year
- ○ Tuition assistance up to $50,000
- ○ Discounts for entertainment and numerous services
- ○ Retirement program after 20 years of service

1.4 million American soldiers actively serve in the five branches of the Armed Forces.

Women make up almost 15% of the U.S. Armed Forces. The Air Force has the highest percentage of women.

Top Three Symbols of the U.S.

The American Flag

The Statue of Liberty

The National Anthem

Source: U.S. Department of Defense

We also show our patriotism through military service. We have one million, four hundred thousand soldiers in the United States. According to the Center for Defense Information, the U.S. by far leads the world in military spending. For fiscal year 2005, the U.S. military budget is at 401 billion dollars. To put these numbers in context, the Center for Arms Control and Non-Proliferation reports that U.S. military spending is eight times larger than China's, whose military budget is at 51 billion, and is the second largest military spender in the world, with Russia following closely behind at 50.8 billion.

Roughly one million of our 1.4 million American servicemen are stationed in the United States. The rest are stationed abroad. Most of our military personnel have been permanently stationed in Germany, Japan, and South Korea. Our military commitments abroad are in the process of change, however, with recent massive deployments in Afghanistan and Iraq.

Many people from other countries have their first contacts with American soldiers stationed abroad, and sometimes the contact is not a positive one. There have been numerous reports of drunkenness in bars and rapes of women who live close to American military bases. In contrast, American soldiers come back with stories of the exciting night life in these foreign countries.

American soldiers who commit crimes abroad are usually tried in U.S. military courts and are frequently acquitted or go unpunished. In South Korea, American soldiers are stationed at the border, the Demilitarized Military Zone, between North and South Korea. In June 2003, two American soldiers ran over and killed two local teenage girls in a training exercise. The soldiers were caught, tried in U.S. military courts and were found not guilty. This incident sparked massive protests in Seoul. Anti-American sentiment has increased due to many incidents by our soldiers abroad.

The American media seldom reports our men in

uniform committing crimes abroad, or their disregard of human rights. The United Nations has proposed an international criminal court to hold soldiers accountable when charged with crimes abroad, but the United States has voted against it and the proposal has not been implemented.

The American military has been an entirely voluntary service since 1973. Many young high school graduates sign up or enlist for two to four years, depending on the branch of service, mainly because of the benefits that the federal government promises.

After completing your service, military benefits include the federal government paying for your college. The U.S. government also helps with a mortgage if veterans want to buy a house, and provides special medical insurance along with many more lifetime benefits.

If you survive the risks and dangers of military service and come back healthy, you will receive many benefits. Military veterans are truly members of a privileged class in American culture. At the end of 2003, *Time* magazine honored "The American Soldier" for its "Person of the Year" issue.

What is freedom to Americans? If you ask Americans, most will answer in a personal, not a political way. They want a home and a good job and to be able to do anything they want. They usually fail to mention the freedom to worship any religion, to move anywhere in the country and other freedoms.

In our presidential elections, there have been times in history where presidents have been elected without the majority of the popular vote. If the presidential candidate wins a majority of electoral votes, the state's entire block of votes goes to the party candidate. Critics of this "winner take all" electoral system point to the possibility of electing a President who loses the popular vote. This has happened in our political history with John Quincy Adams in 1824, Rutherford B. Hayes in 1876, Benjamin Harrison in 1888, and most recently, with George W. Bush in 2000.

We tend to be politically apathetic in this country as fewer than half of eligible Americans vote for the president. The people who do vote usually fall into two parties, the Democrats and the Republicans, with a very small percentage divided into smaller, independent parties. If you divide the 50% of the voting public into two parties of 25% each and then reduce that number to account for those who vote for smaller, independent parties, you will have the true number of people electing the president. In other words, around 20% of the people elect the president of the United States.

Why does the United States have such a low voter turnout? Some people believe the American people are happy with the way things are, the status quo, and do not feel the need to vote. Others may not want to take the time to learn about the issues. These attitudes result in fewer and fewer individuals deciding who will have the political power in the United States.

Shop Till You Drop!

All Roads Lead to the Shopping Mall
Buses usually run express services to the shopping malls across the United States.

Mall-rats
Teens often use the shopping malls as social gathering places. They set trends in fashion that younger children often want to follow.

Children Spend at an Early Age
Through advertising and TV exposure, young American children learn brand names when they are in elementary school. The number of children who are spending on their own is increasing. American children also have a big influence on what kinds of food their parents buy when they do their weekly grocery shopping.

Living with Less
With consumer debt and personal bankruptcies on the rise, a movement to simplify our lives is spreading across the United States as evidenced by recent book titles:

○ *Choosing Simplicity* by Linda Breen Pierce
○ *The Simple Living Guide* by Janet Luhrs

Chapter 18:

Material Girls & Boys

We are the most materialistic nation on the planet. Americans collect more things than most people in other countries can imagine, and we spend an enormous amount of time maintaining them.

Some of our garages are so crammed with junk that the car has to be parked in the driveway or the street.

Many museums in the United States are not showcases of paintings or sculpture; they house collections of ordinary objects instead. There are surfboard museums, guitar museums, and computer museums. You name the object, most likely there is a museum for that object somewhere in the United States.

You can really see our materialism at American birthday parties. They have become a huge business. Parents give their 5 year-olds a party full of expensive entertainment. They rent a site at a restaurant such as *Chuck E. Cheese* and give their children complete freedom. The birthday child and the guests play the machines or games after blowing out the candles on the birthday cake. If parents have the birthday party at home, they often rent a trampoline, an Astro Jump, or hire clowns to paint faces or give pony rides.

Actually, children no longer have to wait for their birthday or Christmas to receive gifts. Parents shower them with toys all year long. An American child's bedroom is filled with not one or two stuffed animals but dozens of them. The number of toys a typical child owns is shocking to people of other countries. Yet a common complaint from American children is that they are bored. How is that possible?

Parents usually plan an elaborate birthday celebration when their children turn 16, especially for girls. Sweet sixteen is seen as a passage to womanhood and many families throw a huge party for their daughters. Some parents even rent a room in a hotel or hall so their daughter and friends can dance until the early morning hours.

Then there is prom night, which is a formal dance in high school. Girls and boys usually wear formal gowns and tuxedos and rent a limo to go the school dance. By the time graduation rolls around, the parties have gotten bigger and the spending more lavish.

This is how the simplest of activities, having a birthday or being with friends, has been commercialized and centered on buying things to display rather than on being with people.

Americans generally believe technology solves problems, not people, or that money can buy most solutions. If their child has a problem, parents buy tutoring sessions. If Americans go camping once a year, they might buy enough equipment to live in the forest for two months.

Is there a counterculture in the United States that offers us an alternative to the materialism? Yes, but it is very small. People who actively try to change their lifestyle to a less materialistic one are usually concerned about the protection of the environment or going back to the simple life.

Shopping

We really don't need human contact, or even have to speak English well, to shop in the United States. Of course, we can buy on-line, as some Americans do. But, more frequently, we go into a shop to touch and handle the merchandise and, in the case of clothes, to try them on. Price tags are openly displayed on the merchandise. In some countries, items are often hidden behind the counter and we must ask the store clerk to see them. In the United States, the price is the same for everyone, even if you have a foreign accent.

We are able to pick up and handle items to inspect them in stores without any obligation to buy them. We can try on clothes for an hour and then walk away with a "No, thanks." Salesclerks demonstrate how electronic items work and provide a lot of information before we decide to buy an item.

In other countries, the pricing of items is very different from ours. The price of something has a range and the customer must bargain for the best price he can get from the seller. In some countries, as soon as the salesclerk finds out you are from out of town or a foreigner, the price may be higher because they assume all foreigners are rich. Or in a department store, the clerk may have some leeway as to what price to charge the customer.

In any case, the negotiation of a price and the need to ask for merchandise behind the counter all demand more human contact and language skills than here.

If we don't see a price tag in the United States, many stores now offer electronic scanners to the consumer in the store. We no longer have to hunt down a salesclerk or wait until we get to the cash register.

A unique feature in American stores is our ability to

return merchandise after we have purchased it. Customer service counters are found in most stores, where we can get a refund, store credit, or an exchange. A refund is given when you return the item you bought, with the receipt, and you want to receive cash back. A store credit is when you don't have the receipt for the item you purchased; the store then gives credit equal to the amount of the item's purchase. An exchange is used when the item purchased is damaged or not working in some way and the customer wants the same thing, but in good condition. You leave the defective item at the customer service counter and look for another similar item in the store without any exchange of money.

Shopping is addictive in the United States. Few of us need an excuse to shop today. There are people who need to shop every day to feel good, true shopaholics. Of course, few foreign visitors escape the seductive power of stores in advertising their wares, and use much of their spare time shopping, too.

Nearly all of our holidays in the United States have lost their original meaning and have turned into shopping holidays. Substantial sales are also tied to a particular day to get us in the door and spending our money.

Of course, if we wait for a sale to be tied to a season, there are only four seasons, and four sales are not nearly enough. This is why we have a President's Day sale, a Memorial Day sale, a Labor Day sale, a Columbus Day sale, a Veterans Day sale, a Thanksgiving sale, and sales before and after Christmas.

In such a competitive business, stores do not merely announce they have reduced prices or discounts. No, it's a war out there. We use violent images of a sword or at least a knife. Prices have been cut. Sales are described as *slashing prices, price cuts* or *blow-outs*. Many Americans buy the daily newspaper just for the ads. Buying a local newspaper in the United States would virtually disappear if it were not for the store ads and customer coupons.

Notes

"Junk is something you keep for years and then throw out two weeks before you need it."

– Source Unknown

The Stagecoach

The stagecoach era only lasted twenty years, 1849-1869, before the railroad put an end to this method of transportation. However brief in our history, the stagecoach has become part of the mythology of our country. It has become a symbol of limitless mobility, adventure and escape. Today, the car and the road trip still express the freedom to move wherever we want.

In Search of the American Cowboy

In American Westerns, we idealize the cowboy, symbolized in John Wayne. Few people know that cowboys usually were very young boys, 12-17 year-olds. Most cowboys retired by the age of 40, making John Wayne more of a romanticized icon than an actor playing an historical role.

American Westerns

Western TV programs such as *Bonanza* and the *Little House on the Prairie*, captured the historical era of the American Frontier.

Chapter 19:

Coast to Coast

I t takes anywhere from three to seven days to drive
across the United States, a country that is 2,800 miles
wide (4,514 kilometers) and 1,200 miles (2,023
kilometers) long.

Many people dream of packing up their belongings in
the car and making a cross-country road trip. A four-hour
plane ride definitely sounds more comfortable, but not
nearly as romantic, as a road trip from one coast to the
other. If you were traveling from the East Coast to the West
in the past, the journey was not even close to being
romantic.

The stagecoach and wagon 150 years ago brought
Midwesterners and some Easterners across the prairies
from St. Louis to San Francisco on a journey that usually
lasted from 4-5 months because of the poor conditions of
the roads.

If you came from the East Coast, you were likely to
take a three-month boat ride, which would take you to

Coast to Coast

How can we tell if someone is from Los Angeles or New York?

Los Angeles

New York

Los Angelenos...	*New Yorkers...*
Go to nail salons	Go to delis
Drink smoothies	Drink black coffee
Carry water bottles	Carry newspapers
Wear sunglasses	Wear raincoats
Wear pastel colors or Hawaiian shirts	Wear a lot of black & closed-toe shoes
Are laid back and mellow	Are hyper & uptight
Use "dude" & first names	Use last names more

Panama. There, you would get off the ship, walk the 10-mile (16 kilometers) strip of land, or go by pack mule to the other side to get to the Pacific Ocean, board another ship when it came, and head north to the first port of call in the United States, San Diego.

Going through Panama was a shortcut. The long way, which many people took, was to take a ship all around the tip of South America, a voyage that could take at least six months.

Today, you can even walk all the way across the country following a national trail that will take you about 18 months. The American Discovery Trail is the "Route 66" for American hikers or bikers. Established in 2000, it is a coast-to-coast trail that stretches across 15 states, and goes through cities, mountains and deserts, and is for serious bikers or hearty back-packers with time on their hands.

Regional Differences

A popular saying reflects the regional differences in the United States. In Boston, people ask what kind of family you come from; in New York, they ask how much money you make, and in Los Angeles, they ask what kind of car you drive.

What people value distinguishes a region, but through radio, television, and now the Internet, our collective consciousness in the United States has grown. Still, local peculiarities identify the major regions.

In the Southeastern part of the United States, the Southern dialect is the most distinguishing factor. People in the southeast of the country speak with a rising and falling intonation, in a drawn-out way known as the Southern Drawl. It sounds something like this, *"Y'all want a cup of tea?"*

The pace of life is also slower in the South. Though the Civil War ended in 1865, almost a hundred forty years ago, some Southerners still harbor ill feelings toward Yankees, since the Northerners won the war. A Confederate flag flew on the county courthouse in South Carolina until only recently, when the Supreme Court forced the flag to be taken down.

The Northeast is full of Yankees. This is what Americans call people living in the northeastern region of the United States, and it is not a term referring to all Americans, as we are sometimes labeled abroad. New Englanders speak quickly, and also have a strong accent. They tend to drop the "r" after vowels, which is a trademark of a Boston accent. They also draw out the "aw" sound so their coffee sounds like *cawfee*.

Americans divide themselves in half at the Mississippi River. This is how we measure what region we are from. Anything west of the Mississippi is considered the West to most Americans. However, there are variations on this theme. If I talk to Californians and tell them I was born in Michigan, they say, "Oh, you're from the East Coast." If I talk to New Yorkers, it's, "Oh, you're from the Midwest. "

Midwesterners, or those people born in Chicago and Detroit and other industrial cities and towns in this region, are mostly immune to many new trends and foreign influences. This is Middle America, where people are more content with where they live than the rest of the population. It is a region of "steady Eddies." Characterized by other regions as being old-fashioned, they move less than Californians but a bit more than New Englanders.

We can move west until we hit Texas. Texas is a state unto itself. It is the only state that declared itself an independent country for ten years. From 1836-1846, it was the Republic of Texas. Texans have been proud of that fact and call themselves the Lone Star state. The Texas state flag carries one star to represent this unique historical independence.

Texas is portrayed in the media as the land of cowboys and gunslingers. This stereotype is reinforced by western-type clothing. Many Texan men wear a big belt buckle and pointy boots to blend into their Texan landscape. The state of Texas is also noted for its tough enforcement of the death penalty. It doesn't just talk about the death penalty, as many states do, but actually practices it. Texas is the state that actually kills the most death row inmates.

Since 1970, Texas has executed 289 people. This is far ahead of the next execution state, Virginia, which has killed 87 people over that same time period. There is a saying, "Don't mess with Texas." If Texas makes you nervous, you can always move west to California.

California is the start-over state. It is where people go when they make a mistake, go bankrupt, get a divorce, get into trouble with the law, or are just feel like they are going nowhere. Why not try California? Nobody knows you or your background. It offers a place to begin a new life with a clean slate.

This notion of moving west and making a fresh start has to do with how California was founded. Gold was discovered in 1848, and California became a state just two years later, completely skipping the intermediate step of being a territory first, because Congress was eager to admit a state with riches.

There was a massive migration of people, called the 49ers, from the East. Most of the 49ers were single men seeking fortunes. While this idea of improving one's lot in life in California stems from the Gold Rush, it is how California is still known today. It's a state that works magic. It's the golden state; it has the Golden Gate.

In California, Los Angeles is the capital of Botox treatments. Keeping a body beautiful is an obsession here. Where else would you find an exercise club on the beach like the one at Venice Beach? There are more nail salons per capita than Boston and its bookstores. The language here is full of *dudes* and *whatevers*, and slang borrowed from surfers.

Since California is such an expensive state to live in today, many people who move to another state are passing it up and heading toward neighboring states. Nevada and Arizona are attracting both immigrants and Americans seeking jobs and lower housing prices.

Among metropolitan cities in the United States, New York City is in a class by itself. Other parts of the country call it neurotic, but it is the only real city in the United States that feels cosmopolitan when compared to European and Asian cities. What we call urban in the United States seems suburban to many foreigners. The rest of American cities qualify as major metropolitan areas by population only. They retain a small-town feel and the access to public services and commerce is minimal compared to New York.

What about nightlife? Nightlife in the United States is also limited to a few major cities. In many American cities, stores close down after dark and the streets are empty because we are afraid of what might happen to us after 10 p.m. Many of us are also ready for bed around that time anyway in order to get up early for work.

In Brazil, Europe, and other parts of the world, nightlife is just beginning at 10 p.m. In Latin American countries in particular, dancing plays a major role in the country's nightlife. You don't need to go to a club to dance, either, as inviting people to your house and dancing the night away is a common practice on weekends. In Taiwan, there are many teahouses and Internet cafes that offer places for young people to gather at night. In the United States, young people tend to go to bars or dance clubs where you will find mainly other young people. Many times, drinking is the primary focus, with very little dancing.

Notes

"In the United States there is more space where nobody is than where anybody is. That is what makes America what it is."

– Gertrude Stein, American writer (1874-1946)

Romance in the U.S.

Kissing and hugging in public are passionate behaviors commonly called making out or public displays of affection. These range from simply hand-holding to grabbing body parts in public.

Americans reactions vary when they see other couples getting physical. Some smile, feel embarrassed or blush and others feel uncomfortable and complain that "it's not polite" or even "it's disgusting." In movies, Americans might call a romantic movie "mushy."

Nicknames for Sweethearts

Americans often use desserts for nicknames when they refer affectionately to each other: Honey, Honeybun, Sweetie, Sweetie pie, Sugar, Sugar pie, Pumpkin. Others: Dear, Darling, Baby, Babe, Precious, Angel, Love and my Better Half.

Classic Pick-Up Lines

- Haven't I seen you before?
- Do you come here often?
- Do you live around here?
- Can I buy you a drink?

Chapter 20:

Mating Rituals

S ex is everywhere in the United States, and available to all. Meanwhile, arranged marriages continue in some parts of the world, and women can be stoned for adultery in other parts of the world.

In the United States, looking for a partner in a country of self-absorbed and insular people is more difficult than ever. You can't marry the boy next door because you barely know your neighbors anymore.

If we didn't widely practice birth control in this country, we would marry a lot earlier than we do. As it is, 26 and 28 years old is the average age for American women and men to tie the knot today. We tend to underestimate the power of birth control and how it affects sexual matters and dating relationships. It is no coincidence that the founder of birth control, Margaret Sanger, was one of 11 siblings.

American movies show couples who meet in one scene and jump into bed in the next. It usually doesn't

Kissing Customs

France – The kissing capital of the world. Start with your left cheek first, normally two kisses are enough, but in Brittany, three is the norm.

Italy – Kissing is for very close friends or family in Italy.

Spain, Austria and Scandinavia – Two kisses. For Spain, you begin the kissing on the right cheek.

Kissing On The Hand – This is considered a great sign of respect and sometimes, adoration.

Kissing On The Head – Shows tender care. Parents sometimes kiss children on their head as a part of a parental blessing.

Blowing A Kiss In The Air – When we are far away from someone, we send them a kiss by air-mail.

Sealed with a Kiss

Where did signing a letter with three XXX's for kisses and three OOO's for hugs come from?

This tradition, also called SWAK, comes from medieval Europe, at a time when many people could not read and write. An important document was usually signed with an X, which was then kissed as a sign of sincerity.

Latin Lovers

In Latin, there are three different words for a kiss, depending on the level of intimacy:

- ○ An acquaintance kiss – *basium*
- ○ A close friend's or relative's kiss – *osculum*
- ○ A lover's kiss – *suavium*

happen that fast. Movies, designed to tell a life story in two hours, omit the development of a relationship and fast-forward to the bed as a way to establish an intimate, physical relationship on the screen.

American men and women tend to be sexually active yes, but not after one date and not with just anybody. Unlike the one-night stands you see in the movies, American women usually go through a series of stages, feelings and commitment before they jump into bed with a boyfriend. In the 1980's, the fear of getting AIDS changed the dating scene in the United States. Carefree sex could now have deadly consequences, and the condom came back to life as a method of prevention of sexually-transmitted diseases.

We are re-discovering our virginity in the United States from campaigns in public schools whose slogan is "Just Say No," to born-again Christians who have decided to become born-again virgins.

After many years of high rates of teenage pregnancy in the United States, the number of pregnancies has leveled off in recent years. Some of this is due to the scare of AIDS, and part of it may be because of the pregnancy prevention taught in schools.

Sexual education is taught in public schools as early as elementary school. Basic short videos begin teaching sex in a scientific way. As students go through junior high, the nature of what they learn becomes less scientific and more practical. By the time Americans reach high school, many are sexually active. They learn about sexually-transmitted diseases, including AIDS, and the focus turns to pregnancy prevention.

Schools have targeted not just women but also men for pregnancy prevention. One such program, called *Baby Think It Over*, requires both male and female high schoolers to take a 7-pound (3.2 kilos) baby doll home over the weekend and care for it 24-hours a day. The electronic doll has been programmed by the teacher to be

Matters of the Heart

When you care about other people or are very giving to others, we say you have **a heart of gold or have a big heart.**

On the other hand, if you are mean and lack compassion, you are **heartless** or **cold-hearted**. When you thank someone and you want to emphasize your appreciation, you can thank him or her **from the bottom of your heart**.

Will You Marry Me?

The average American engagement lasts 16 months, according to the Condé Nast Bridal Group.

○ The average amount spent on a traditional American wedding - $22,000.

○ Popular honeymoon destinations for American newlyweds: Las Vegas, Hawaii, U.S. Virgin Islands, Jamaica and the Bahamas.

○ In Taiwan, the groom's family must pay for all of the wedding expenses. This means the groom's family also decides on the details for the wedding.

especially fussy at certain times, so the baby cries when it is hungry or has a wet diaper. This program has been successful in teaching teenagers in middle and high schools that having a baby is a constant responsibility.

Many American young adults are skeptical and cynical about marriage, since many of them are children of divorced parents. They are afraid of commitment and afraid to repeat their parents' mistakes. As a consequence, many people will go out on a regular basis but if the "M" word, or marriage, is brought up, well, the mere discussion of the topic may cause the couple to fight over commitment. It may even cause the couple to break up if one of them is not ready.

The Internet has changed the dating process, as on-line dating is becoming more popular with young people. There are chat rooms. What if we are in a relationship with someone we see every day and yet think we are in love with another person on the Internet? Suddenly, the vocabulary we have used for centuries doesn't quite work to describe Internet relationships.

The cell phone has also changed dating. Does a conversation count as a meeting time? What if we are talking with the person more than going out with them? The ability to reach someone anytime has made dating a less important event. Of course, we can always turn off the cell phone, which may send a message that we are upset with another person or that we want to be left alone.

Today, the bar scene is limited. Monday night is football watching night in the United States, and many men are found in front of the television screen in bars. Some women avoid bars altogether thinking that it is a place for single men who are only looking to pick up girls for sex and not a relationship.

Singles have come up with a new solution to meeting many people in a short period of time, *speed dating*. They pay $20-30 dollars and have a user name to remain anonymous and to meet many dates in one evening. For speed dating, there is a group with an equal number of men and women and usually of the same age range. The women stay at their tables and the men change seats every few minutes. In a matter of seven to ten minutes, the date can be asked just about anything except his or her age, real name, occupation and residence. The idea is to focus on what the person is really like. The dates try to get to know each other as fast as they can. Later, they can tell the agency who they have liked and the agency gives further contact information. Singles get to meet a number of people in a two-hour period. This is much more intense search for a mate than trying to do this hit and miss with one person. In this date selection process, first impressions are extremely important.

Work is a common place to meet someone, but what happens if you have chosen a female-dominated job such as nursing, teaching and social service jobs, or a male-dominated one like construction, electrical engineering, or the police force?

When we date, many expressions are used to convey the nuances of not fully committing to one person. When we flirt with someone or show we like him or her through eye contact or by dropping verbal hints, we are *"hitting on someone."* When we are physically affectionate with someone at parties and in cars, we are *"making out."* If we change our minds about a person who we were once so passionate about, we ignore him, or *"brush him off."*

Young people plan and cancel dates or *"make and break dates."* There is the *"double date"* when two couples go out together and which is less threatening for those who are unsure about the potential partner. If we want to get to know someone and don't know how to begin, we might start by *"feeding someone a line"* that goes something like, *"Haven't I met you somewhere?"*

If you meet someone at a party for the first time and later go somewhere else to get to know the person better, *"you have been picked up"* or *"you picked someone up,"* depending on who took the initiative or *"made the first move."*

"Are you a couple?" means are you boyfriend and girlfriend? *"I'm seeing someone"* does not necessarily mean that you have an exclusive sexual relationship with another person. We try to avoid promising to be faithful to someone, or at least we try hard to act unattached and free of commitment. We want to appear *"still available."*

Some Americans change girlfriends or boyfriends so often that they joke among themselves asking, *"Who is it this time?"* Many think of it as a game. If the person is not a sincere man or woman and goes out with many different people, we say, *"He's a player,"* or *"She's a player."*

Young people frequently go out with the opposite sex just for companionship and friendship in the United States. A romantic relationship is not assumed but can be sometimes questioned by others. When people ask the couple what their relationship is, a common answer is, *"We're just friends."*

Americans usually have a very romantic idea about love, but at the same time, we are cynical and distrusting of true love. We expect a lot. Some of us write exactly what we want in personal ads published in the newspaper or posted on the Internet. Anyone can see what we have to offer. We have announced our great personality and perfectly-shaped bodies, and then we tell you what we are looking for in great detail. Now if you fit the characteristics described in the paragraph, you can respond to the number in our ad and leave a message. We who have placed the ad, call or e-mail you back and you may have *"a blind date"* as a result. Seeing someone by keeping contact only through e-mail messages and never meeting the person is quite a bit like going out on a blind date.

With all of these new options for dating in the United States, genuine emotions and sincere intentions are a bit hard to come by today. How can we compete with the messages of the professional kind? You go into our drugstores and see aisles filled with greeting cards. The greeting card industry makes a lot of money from our emotions. Personally writing down our sentiments is no longer required. Similar to voice mail options and computer-generated messages, these store-bought cards do it for us. They are artificially sweet, but we buy one of these cards anyway. It's much easier than trying to reflect on our own genuine feelings.

My dear, darling, honey, sweetie, pumpkin, sweetheart, babe, we write. Any of these terms of endearment will do, as long as we begin our affectionate greeting at the top of the card before the text message. The rest is filled out for us, so we hurry down to the bottom of the card. We write as many X X X's and O O O's as we want, we sign our name on our $3.99 greeting card and we're done.

Maintaining a romantic relationship through e-mail poses a challenge today. There is often a false intimacy that comes with relationships kept alive by long-distance e-mails. Just because we are able to write a person any time does not necessarily mean our relationship is any stronger. Frequency of contact does not automatically reflect the quality of a relationship.

In the past, we received immediate feedback from a person in a face-to-face encounter. Today, feedback from other people is often reduced to a couple of words in an e-mail reply the next day, which may simply read, "good idea," or "sorry." This brief response will likely arrive in our inbox and could leave us with the feeling of "Is that all?"

Electronic communication is so common and so new, we do not really know its long-term effects on our human relationships. What is certain, however, is that by the click of a mouse, we can learn how people from other parts of the world are both different and yet alike in many ways.

Notes

"Love is temporary insanity curable by marriage."

– Ambrose Bierce
American short-story writer, (1842-1914)

Bibliography

Bennett, Lerone Jr. *Before the Mayflower: A History of Black America*. New York:Penguin, 1984.

Bureau of Justice. *Homicide Trends in the United States*, Washington, D.C., 2000.

Chakravorti, Sujit, and Timothy McHugh. "Why do we use so many checks?" *Economic Perspectives Report*, Federal Reserve Bank of Chicago, 2002.

Interagency Council on the Homeless. *Homelessness: Programs and the People They Serve*, U.S. Bureau of the Census, 1999.

Killias, Martin, John van Kesteren, and Martin Rindlisbacher. "Guns, violent crime and suicide in 21 countries." in *Canadian Journal of Criminology*, vol. 43/4, October 2002.

Klein, Jim and Martha Olsen. "How GM Destroyed the U.S. Rail System." *Auto Free Times*, vol. 10, January 30, 1999.

Kosmin, Barry A. and Seymour P. Lachman. *One Nation Under God*. New York: Harmony Books, 1993.

Kosmin, Barry A. and Egon Mayer. *American Religious Identification Survey*, New York: City University of New York, 2001.

Lederer, Richard. *The Miracle of English*. New York: Pocket Books, 1991.

Mayer, Don. "Institutionalizing Overconsumption: The Oil Industry and Destruction of Public Transport." in *The Business of Consumption*, eds. Laura Westra and Patricia H. Werhane, June 1998.

McCrum, Robert, William Cran, and Robert MacNeil. *The Story of English*. New York: Viking Penguin Press, 1986.

Menzel, Peter. *Material World*. New York: Random House, 1993.

National Center for Educational Statistics. "Pursuing Excellence: A Study of U.S. Twelfth-Grade Mathematics and Science Achievement in International Context." *Third International Mathematics and Science Study*, Washington D.C., 1998.

National Center for Health Statistics. "An Overview of Nursing Home Facilities." *National Nursing Home Survey*, Advance Data No. 311, March 1, 2000.

National Geographic Society. *Global Geographic Literacy Survey*, National Geographic-Roper, 2002.

Pitman, Joanna. *On Blondes*. New York: Bloomsbury, 2003.

Pucher, John and Lewis Dijkstra. "Making Walking and Cycling Safer: Lessons from Europe," in *Transportation Quarterly*, Vol. 54, No. 3, Summer 2000.

Selected Internet Websites

American Civil Liberties Union. Reports on the number of prisoners in the United States. (www.aclu.org)

American Discovery Trail. Information on the coast-to-coast trail. (www.discoverytrail.org)

American Educational Statistics (www.nces.ed.gov)

Amnesty International. Reports on executions by country. (www.amnesty.org)

Animal Legal Defense Fund. (www.aldf.org)

Bureau of Justice. Reports on crime, victims and homicide trends in the U.S. (www.ojp.usdoj.gov/bjs/cvict.htm)

Chivalry. (www.chivalrytoday.com)

The Death Penalty Information Center. Statistics on the death penalty. (www.deathpenaltyinfo.org)

Divorce Reform. (www.divorcereform.org)

Federal Bureau of Investigation. The Uniform Crime Reports Program collects crime data in the United States, including the number of hate crimes. (www.fbi.gov/ucr)

Frivolous lawsuits. (www.power-of-attorneys.com)

National League of Cities. Reports on curfews in the U.S. (www.nlc.org.)

National Center of Aging. (www.ncoa.org)

U.S. Census Bureau. Population and demographic data. (www.census.gov)

Index

About the Author

During the wee hours of January 26, 1958, the author became a citizen of East Detroit, a small suburb where people live on square subdivision plots, hemmed in by the fear of going too far south and reaching downtown Detroit, or too far east and falling in the Great Lakes of Michigan.

There she was raised, received her college education, and trained in the way a good wholesome girl from the Midwest should go. She didn't go that way. First, she majored in international relations, and then she had to see those faraway places with strange-sounding names.

Her passion for cultures other than her own led her to Mexico where she worked as a reporter while trying to master the subjunctive tense and 29 names for hot peppers. In New York City, she freelanced for newspapers and magazines, counseled Vietnamese refugees, copyedited books for lawyers, and interpreted in the local courts.

She now lives in San Diego with her Ecuadorian husband, Angel, who lets her speak Spanish with a fierce American accent, and her daughter, Sonia. She has taught English to international students for more than 15 years.